# Voi
# Psychotic
# Experiences

C000176149

## A reconsideration of recovery and diversity

OLM-Pavilion

Edited by Ruth Chandler and Mark Hayward

# Voicing Psychotic Experiences

## A reconsideration of recovery and diversity

Edited by Ruth Chandler and Mark Hayward

OLM-Pavilion

# Voicing Psychotic Experiences
## A reconsideration of recovery and diversity

Ruth Chandler and Mark Hayward

© OLM-Pavilion 2009

**Published by:**
OLM-Pavilion
Richmond House
Richmond Road
Brighton BN2 3RL
UK
**Tel:** 01273 623222
**Fax:** 01273 625526
**Email:** info@pavpub.com
**Web:** www.pavpub.com

A catalogue record for this book is available from the British Library.

ISBN: 978 1 84196 252 8

OLM-Pavilion is the leading training and development provider and publisher in the health, social care and allied fields, providing a range of innovative training solutions underpinned by sound research and professional values. We aim to put our customers first, through excellent customer service and good value.

**Pavilion editor:** Sanaz Nazemi
**Cover and page design:** Emma Garbutt, OLM-Pavilion
**Cover image:** 'Walking Barefoot Through the Meadow Grass' by Gina Bold www.ginabold.com; The Otherside Gallery

Printed on paper from a sustainable resource by Ashford Press, Southampton.

# Contents

# Foreword

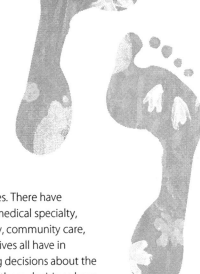

This book appears at an exciting time in the history of mental health services. There have been many previous initiatives in mental health: the rise of psychiatry as a medical specialty, moral treatment, institutionalisation, deinstitutionalisation, social psychiatry, community care, anti-psychiatry and critical psychiatry, to name but a few. What these initiatives all have in common is that they involve one group of people –'professionals' – making decisions about the lives of another group – 'patients'. The views of people actually affected by these decisions have been neither sought nor used.

Times are changing. For the last few decades, a quiet global revolution has been underway, as people with lived experience of mental illness begin to find and use their voice. *Voicing Psychotic Experiences* follows in a proud tradition of publications by people who speak from within the experience of mental illness, rather than as an external observer. Early pioneers from the USA (Deegan, 1996; Chamberlin, 1978) New Zealand (O'Hagan, 1996) and Scotland (Coleman, 1999) broke the taboo by talking about the experience of mental illness and mental health services. Recent years have seen many more stories emerging, with compilations in England at local (Carson *et al*, 2008; Cornwall Partnership NHS Trust, 2008) and national (McIntosh, 2005) levels. What these narratives all have in common is a focus on the experience of living, with remarkable testimonies about the possibility of change and transformation. Recovery, it transpires, is indeed open to all.

There are lessons to be learned by mental health services through hearing the voice of lived experience. Some of the positive supports from mental health services that are identified by the contributors to this book include counselling, medication, getting the diagnosis right, cognitive behavioural therapy (CBT), and the involvement of skilled caring and hopeful professionals. However, many people find a way forward in their life that is outside of, or in non-patient roles within the mental health system. Some of the turning points described in this book include entering a close relationship, developing spiritual balance, connecting with nature, training and supporting others about mental illness, training as a mental health professional such as a social worker or a clinical psychologist, voluntary work, support from the family, finding accepting friends, stopping contact with unhelpful people, visiting a healer, education, telling one's story to others, challenging discrimination, using humour and accepting oneself. So the stark lesson for mental health services is that they can be part of the solution, but not the whole solution. The job of the mental health system is to support the individual in finding their own way forward in their own life (Slade, 2009) whether or not that way forward is consistent with clinical guidelines.

Yet, this book goes further. The two editors separately bring lived experience and professional experience of mental illness. In this, they model the partnership relationship of recovery – supporting mental health services of the future. The ability to apply theoretical frameworks of knowledge and evidence-based interventions to the complexity of human experience are contributions of the professional. The ability to communicate values, preferences and goals, and to recognise oppressive assumptions, are contributions of lived experience. Partnership involves the use of these two forms of knowledge to create intellectual and emotional space for critical thinking and reflection, as modelled in Chapter 6, and the conclusion of this book. The goal of a partnership relationship is to be, as the editors put it, hospitable to difference. This book illustrates how workers in the mental health system can engage with the experience of people with psychosis, whilst not imposing their own meaning on those experiences.

For people experiencing psychosis and their family and friends, this book will give hope. For people working in the mental health system, *Voicing Psychotic Experiences* will support workers in their goal of seeing the person not the illness. It should be widely read.

Mike Slade
**Reader in Health Services Research, Institute of Psychiatry, King's College London**

## References

Carson J, Holloway F, Wolfson P & McNary M (eds) (2008) *Recovery Journeys: Stories of coping with mental health problems*. London: South London and Maudsley NHS Foundation Trust.

Chamberlin J (1978) *On Our Own: Patient-controlled alternatives to the mental health system*. New York: Hawthorn.

Coleman R (1999) *Recovery – An alien concept*. Gloucester: Hansell Publishing.

Cornwall Partnership NHS Trust (2008) *Recovery Stories. Cornish journeys of hope*. St Austell: Cornwall Partnership Trust.

Deegan P (1996) Recovery as a journey of the heart. *Psychosocial Rehabilitation Journal* **19** 91–97.

McIntosh Z (2005) *From Goldfish Bowl to Ocean: Personal accounts of mental illness and beyond*. London: Chipmunka Publishing.

O'Hagan M (1996) Two accounts of mental distress. In: J Read & J Reynolds (eds). *Speaking Our Minds*. London: Macmillan.

Slade M (2009) *Personal Recovery and Mental Illness. A guide for mental health professionals*. Cambridge: Cambridge University Press.

# Notes on the contributors

**Steven West** is the widower of Shirley West and father to Ryan. He is a person who experiences psychosis and uses services, and delivers training with *Psychosis Revisited*.

**Becky Shaw** is a fellow of the Institute of Mental Health and has both used and worked as a volunteer in the mental health services for 16 years. Her background is in research and education. Becky teaches within a variety of settings, including the school of nursing at Nottingham University and at the clinical psychology department at Nottingham Trent and Leicester Universities. She has run a mental health self-help group for 15 years and supports other people who experience mental health distress towards recovery. She was one of the original reviewers for the health care commission and was also a reviewer for the joint reviews for the Commission for Social Care Inspectorate. She has led research and evaluation projects through a variety of organisations, including mental health media and an independent research project in education. Her current projects include leading a research team as chief investigator around the experience of having a mental health crisis and of using the crisis resolution and home treatment teams within Nottinghamshire and Leicestershire Mental Health Trusts. She has written a number of articles and recently published two books.

**Anne Beales** is currently the Director of Service User Involvement at Together – working for the well-being of those with needs specifically related to having mental health problems. As someone who has accessed services, the hope is that this experience enhances her effectiveness in this job. Anne is a member of service user groups at regional levels and alongside this she is serving as a Management Committee member of the National Survivor User Network. She was recently one of two service users to be appointed as a Service User Consultant to the NHS Confederation Mental Health Network Management Board representing the Network. She also sits on the National Committee for Gender Equality and Women's Mental Health. Anne was awarded an MBE in November 2007 for her work in setting up and establishing the Capital project. Although this award is presented to individuals, it does however reflect the work and efforts of all the members of the project.

**Big Roy** is a nature lover and supporter of green living. He is a person who experiences psychosis and delivers training with *Psychosis Revisited*.

**Mark Edgar** was a chorister at King's College Cambridge, music scholar at Lancing College and choral exhibitioner at Selwyn College Cambridge where he read history. He was awarded a Master of Arts in 1995 and a Post Graduate Certificate in Education (PGCE) in 2000. He has worked in both education and mental health, including at Mind, Rethink, Kent Social Services and South Kent College. Currently, he is the first Mental Well-being Adviser at the University of Hertfordshire.

**Moira Green** is living proof that mental health issues can actually enrich your life.

**Emma Harding** is just starting her career as a clinical psychologist. Most of her experience prior to clinical psychology training was in vocational services, helping people with mental health needs to access employment. She has schizophrenia herself and has had to negotiate her career within a society that is often ill-informed about mental distress. Emma feels passionately about helping people recognise that 'mad' does not mean 'bad' or 'incapable'. She has campaigned against stigma with the charity Rethink and was a service user representative on the first treatment guidelines for schizophrenia developed by NICE. Emma has campaigned for mental health rights on many issues, but defines herself as a collaborator rather than an external activist, having worked in NHS mental health services for 11 years.

**Ruth Chandler** is an independent recovery trainer and consultant from West Sussex. She has worked in the voluntary and statutory sectors and specialises in service user and carer-led practice and policy innovations. She is a mother and grandmother to be, and lifelong student of philosophy, theology, literature and cultural studies. She is also a person who has experienced psychosis.

**Mark Hayward** is a husband, father, committed Christian and supporter of West Ham United Football Club. He works as a tutor on the clinical psychology training programme at the University of Surrey, and as the Director of Research within Sussex Partnership NHS Foundation Trust. Mark's understanding of psychotic experience and recovery has been significantly enhanced through time spent with people who have personal experience of pyschosis.

# Acknowledgements

We would like to acknowledge the contributions of all those who have been part of the development and experience of *Psychosis Revisited*, especially Alison Blank, Thurstine Basset, Anne Cooke and Martin Aldred.

We would also like to thank those people who stood by us on the more personal aspects of this journey: Rachel, Kevin, Shirley and Ryan.

# Introduction

Ruth Chandler and Mark Hayward

## Introducing recovery

'Recovery' is in vogue (Hayward & Slade, 2008; Shepherd *et al*, 2008; Slade & Hayward, 2007). Whether conceptualised as a process, a vision, an outlook or a guiding principle, recovery has prompted debate about mental health care for people with severe mental health problems. The ability of people to get 'better' following some form of psychotic breakdown is not newsworthy; it has been known for many years that the majority of such people go on to lead satisfying lives (Harrison *et al*, 2001). Introduced into mental health discourse primarily by individuals who have experienced recovery, the novel contribution of recovery has been to focus attention on the needs and aspirations of those individuals for whom psychotic experiences and associated distress might be an ongoing aspect of their existence; people whose difficulties might previously have been labelled as chronic – for whom the spark of hope may have been systematically extinguished as they were perceived as unable to 'return to health'. For these individuals, the pertinent statement might not be 'recovery from symptoms/illness/distress', as these experiences may continue. Rather, the focus might shift on to 'recovery to and by what means?' How is it possible to live a '*satisfying, hopeful and contributing life, even with limitations imposed by the illness?*' (Anthony, 1993).

Listening, searching for meaning and supporting journeys of recovery in a hopeful manner are some of the ways in which people who experience psychosis can be assisted as they seek to understand their unusual experiences and attempt to claim or reclaim quality in their lives. Each of these tasks is explored within the second edition of *Psychosis Revisited* (Basset *et al*, 2007), a manual for the training of mental health workers, service users and carers. The manual is based upon an innovative report from The British Psychological Society (2000), *Understanding Mental Illness: Recent advances in understanding mental illness and psychotic experiences* and draws upon a range of social and psychological perspectives with which to understand the lives, hopes and aspirations of people who experience psychosis. Most importantly, the manual draws extensively upon an under-utilised source of knowledge – the understandings of people who have personal experience of psychosis. How are psychotic experiences understood in the context of people's life histories; what might enable or hinder processes of recovery and how might mental health workers assist? Each of these questions is considered across the two days of the workshop as the participants are increasingly encouraged to reflect upon their own practices and uncertainties and consider possibilities for change.

The views of workshop participants have been explored and feedback was wholeheartedly positive (Houghton *et al*, 2006). Themes from the analysis of qualitative data highlighted how the workshop had raised awareness of the importance of everyday human qualities when working with people who experience psychosis, such as warmth, being friendly, listening and showing concern – '*Little things can have a big impact. I've always suspected this – nice to hear it said*'. In these respects, there was a sense of participants feeling validated in their desire to respond intuitively and respectfully to service users, *'To treat each client as the individual they are'* (Houghton *et al*, 2006).

Participants also spoke of the value of time to reflect upon hope as an essential ingredient in recovery – *'nurturing the spark of hope … most important'*. This is particularly significant for a group of people who may have used services for long periods. Many participants were able to acknowledge a pervasive hopelessness amongst themselves and colleagues, and the part they could play in assisting their clients in developing and working towards aspirations. One participant commented on *'how negative you become without realising and [I learned] how to be more hopeful'* (Houghton *et al*, 2006).

The service user trainers who have been involved in the development of the manual have also found their journey to have been enormously positive. Steven West, involved with *Psychosis Revisited* from the outset, speaks of feeling ' *…respected, valued and listened to … increased self-confidence and a sense of legitimacy'* as a result of the work he does. Alternatively, Becky Shaw speaks of service user involvement being important to her, *'as it means I can help staff to realise that it's not miracle science to help someone. All you need to do is show you care about the person you are helping, listen to what they need and help them with this in the way they want to do it'*.

Becky and Steven's recovery journeys do not involve a move away from services, but rather, they constituted a change in attitude towards the use of services. Emphasis is placed upon the ability of the individual in distress to cope with and manage their distressing experiences, then turn attention to further processes that may facilitate moving on – processes that may be directed towards defining the self in relational, social and occupational (rather than illness) terms. In this sense, the 're' (meaning again) part of recovery can be misleading. For some people, reclaiming aspects of previously valued quality in their lives will be sought after. For others, there may never have been any discernable quality, so sources of quality may need to be claimed (or discovered) for the first time. Yet others may move to a position of greater understanding and compassion (as a consequence of their distress) that allows them to look back on previously valued quality from a different perspective and acknowledge its limitations. What is the bottom line? The process of getting 'better' is defined relative to the experiences and expectations of each individual, rather than through the imposition of an explanatory model that 'privileges' symptom reduction as a necessary dimension of improvement.

## Recovery for whom?

As suggested above, the idea that clients should be supported to enhance the quality of their lives is not rocket science. Rather, it is a common sense position that most new workers take into mental health services and should also be the expectation of people using them. However, the reality is often very different. Over reliance on medical treatments, limited resources and hopeless expectations can create obstacles to recovery, which in turn may become organisationally embedded. While we write in the assumption that most mental health workers decide to work in this field out of a genuine desire to help, they can often find themselves in the unhelpful and frustrating position of unwittingly maintaining distress.

It is now widely recognised that acute inpatient care is not necessarily the place to recuperate (Hughes *et al*, 2008). This recognition is reflected in the greater emphasis on home treatment and crisis intervention, which are based on the idea that the least time in acute inpatient care is the best option for people that experience mental distress. However, acute inpatient care is frequently the place where people that experience psychosis go when they feel very distressed. While there are innovative practices out there, for example early intervention teams, 'symptoms' of psychotic experience are frequently the point at which home treatment and crisis resolution teams refer on to a more 'appropriate' service. A person who experiences psychosis may also be regarded as unsuitable and/or too vulnerable for most forms of talking therapy available to people experiencing other forms of mental distress. While we hope to be proven wrong, a person who experiences multiple episodes of psychosis is still much more likely to be subjected to compulsory home treatment than offered an employment coach under the changes to the Mental Health Act. Employers that see people who experience psychosis as a resource rather than a potential risk are still a dream rather than an actuality for most people that have or have had experience of psychosis.

Why should this be so? If recovery is in vogue, why is it still the case that the distress of people whose reality is substantially different to the reality of mental health workers have less therapeutic options available to them? If most people who choose to work in mental health do so out of a genuine desire to help, what obstacles to recovery stand in the way of this desire? Why do people who experience psychosis continue to encounter greater degrees of stigma and hopeless expectation than someone whose 'symptoms' may seem more familiar? Anyone looking for a one size fits all answer to these questions is bound for disappointment, as psychological, social/cultural, political and medical interpretations of psychotic experience are all likely to influence understandings. At the centre of any helpful understanding will be the meaning made by the person experiencing psychosis, such meaning being made within different contexts.

Within the *Psychosis Revisited* training manual, the extent to which recovery is defined as service or service user led was also shown to vary a great deal. Two models are singled out to illustrate this difference and were chosen because, for us, they appeared to represent the best approaches to recovery from each perspective. Repper and Perkins (2003) offer a compelling account of multiple recovery pathways defined by people in recovery. Here it is made very clear that the understandings and interventions of mental health professionals may not be the appropriate place to start. Recovery defined by professional contexts miss the point of recovery defined by the many contexts (stories) of people in recovery. This is a tempting vision and it is easy to be swept away by it. It is the case that professional contexts have historically tended to see themselves as the only context by which recovery is defined, missing the many contexts through which the meaning of recovery is shaped by a person. But what about the many people who look to services for help in their recovery process? What about those who have been rendered passive and institutionalised and constructed as 'beyond recovery' by poor-quality interventions in the past?

Recovery, defined by the people in recovery, assumes a level of interpretative agency that may not yet exist or has been undermined by interventions that act as if the interpretation of service users does not exist. Helen Glover (2008) points to the way illness saturated environments replace the multiple contexts of identity that have active agency with passive illness determined meanings. She cites her own identity prior to becoming unwell as made up of many roles: friend, wife, a person who loves travel and a gym goer. In an illness-saturated environment these roles are systematically replaced. For example, Helen no longer went to the gym because her support workers took her for walks and replaced her friendship network. The role of wife was replaced by 'cared for' and that of her husband by 'carer', erasing the mutual care that had existed between them. She no longer travelled because her illness got in the way. As time went by, Helen's new identity was defined solely within these terms, shrinking her horizons of expectation to the expectations others held for her. For Helen, recovery is best defined as a process of 'self-righting'; as a removal of the obstacles to a person's active identity. We cannot assume, however, that everyone starts out with an established identity or a horizon of expectation to be undermined. For many people, the building blocks for interpretative agency have never been in place; for example, the confidence that what one says has value or the communication skills to express this. Recovery in this framework may be more like the process of discovery of qualities and potentials for being and doing that were not thought possible before.

Anthony Sheehan's adaptation of the Ohio recovery model is of particular relevance for both groups of people (NIMHE, 2004). Moving from passive and unconscious dependency through to conscious interdependence, Sheehan offers a structured and sober definition of recovery in which services can work with service users that have become passive and institutionalised to a position where it is possible to imagine and develop recovery outcomes different from those embedded in the model. The virtue of this definition is that it is much easier to measure than the more open-ended approach offered by Repper and Perkins and, therefore, much easier to embed organisationally. However, the task still remains of supporting the interpretative agency of people that experience psychosis to define recovery for themselves. The practice innovation of this collection is to identify ways to make room for this agency and bridge the gap between doing it to and doing it with.

## Language and power: unpacking oppositional dialogue

We want to avoid an either/or approach to any recovery 'model', even those that define themselves through not being a model. Both are effective for different people and both have practice implications that can be usefully held together. Given that recovery is 'an idea whose time has come' (Shepherd et al, 2008), it is worth thinking about how recovery can embrace the diversity of recovery pathways without creating a new orthodoxy or 'metamodel' about what recovery is (or isn't) or what it should become. There is a growing consensus that any one size fits all approach is doomed to fail. Recovery takes shape differently in different services, regions and countries. In the UK, for example, it would be naïve to suggest that government enthusiasm for employment-related recovery initiatives does not go hand in hand with a political desire to reduce the amount of people drawing incapacity benefit. At the same time, it would also be naïve to suggest that employment is not a meaningful part of many recovery pathways. For others still, work may be too stressful a part of life to be meaningful, or may involve distressing contact with discriminatory attitudes and organisational structures. The lived reality of multiple recovery pathways is that each is distinct and, as with all experience, is far more complex and messy than the neat systems we would like to fit them into.

With this complexity in mind, we want to unpack some of the issues of language and power that simplify the way knowledge about people that experience psychosis is made and offer reflection on recovery and diversity in a group of people that, superficially, do not appear that diverse at all. It is fair to suggest that there has been a tendency to frame recovery within an oppositional mode of expression in the UK. Many service users and survivors of services have been vocal in pointing to the (very real) limits and negative effects of services that do not engage with them as people whose views matter and are of equal value to those held by service providers. The other side of the coin is that, historically, statutory mental health services have not been commissioned or resourced to work with a notion of recovery beyond the reduction of clinical symptoms whereas the voluntary sector has emerged in gaps in statutory provision. It has been important to expose these gaps as they have existed and continue to exist. There are real and justified fears that the term 'recovery' is being co-opted by service providers (statutory and voluntary) while maintaining a business-as-usual approach. It needs to be stated emphatically that rebranding a service 'recovery' or including the word 'recovery' in a logo is not the same as practising in a recovery-oriented manner. However, there is also a sense in which mutual suspicions between service users and service providers can also sustain an unhelpful construction of professionals as not service users and/or survivors of services, and the same may be said in reverse.

Where does this 'not' come from? At a very basic level, thinking in terms of either/or is a way of mapping the world. This is 'not' that. Language is made up of many such conventions (rules), which contain implicit assumptions that are normalising and which organise thought in oppositional categories. Black is 'not' white. Insane is 'not' sane. Outside is 'not' inside. This is 'not' always a bad thing. Categories are needed to act in social ways. If I assume, for example, that by wearing a suit I will be presenting a formal appearance, I am also making a statement about what is 'not' formal. The dress codes that attend many social contexts make this rule explicit. If I turn up wearing jeans, I will be dressed incorrectly and am unlikely to gain entry. In this way, the context defines what should be normal in its sphere. The people that gain entry are in the 'certain knowledge' that I am in the company of lots of other 'normal' people that, superficially, appear 'just like me'. In so doing, the social 'place' of the suit wearer is affirmed and made concrete in these operations.

Bourdieu's concept of *habitus* is useful for thinking through the above (1990). That is '*the embodied rituals of everydayness by which a given culture produces and sustains belief in its own "obviousness"*' (Butler, 1997a). As the word *habitus* suggests, the everyday rituals, rules and practices that make up social reality are literally acquired habits, structures and actions, which are so commonplace that one no longer turns to question their ideological content. Thinking in black and white is a particularly easy habit to slip into. For example, it is a common practice in many workplaces for staff and service users to keep cups and tea-making facilities in different places. One would rarely question this habit and there may be good health and safety reasons for it. However, for a person using the service for the first time, having cups and tea-making facilities in different places also marks off who is staff and who is not in an unstated way. What is normal for a group, usually comes to the fore when the habitual rules are broken. For example, asking somebody to leave the 'wrong' tea area would make the tacit rule visible. The combination of lots of unstated habits create boundaries, some of which are useful and some of which can be stigmatising if they do not relate to any function other than marking off who is staff and who is not.

Languages have similar 'legal' and 'illegal' moves. One can be out of place in language in a similar way to turning up at a social function wearing the wrong clothes. There is nothing wrong with this kind of rule in a relevant context. Uniforms can be great social levellers, at school, for example, or exemplify pride in occupation, as in the armed services. However, these can be disempowering rules in mental health if the power to name/know expresses predefined expectations about what people who experience psychosis can do and what they can become. Imagine if, on being asked to leave the 'wrong tea area' in a service you either use or work in, it was also suggested that being in the wrong space was a 'symptom' of your faulty reasoning to begin with. Suppose that you object to being told to leave this space without a better explanation. Would your objection be regarded as reasonable or as further evidence of your challenging behaviour?

*Habitus* is a two-way street. The everyday rituals, rules and practices that make up the social reality of service users can close down receptiveness and willingness to listen to mental health workers. When people who experience psychosis define themselves as 'not' being professionals, the exclusion of the 'them/us' has been repeated by another set of speakers. Constructing group identity in relation to those named outside it is also disempowering to mental health workers too and especially those at the frontline. Here it is quite possible to receive a double whammy of negativity through being placed at the bottom end of a service hierarchy with performance targets to meet and at the receiving end of lived distress that they may not feel they have the confidence, skills or supervisory support to address.

Spirals of hopelessness thrive in the conditions described above, making it difficult for people who provide services and people who experience psychosis to see ways to move creatively out of the impasses they invoke. Nevertheless, it is simply not the case that frontline mental health workers and people who experience psychosis stand on a level playing field in the hopelessness stakes. Perkins and Dilks (1992) point to the different worlds of mental health workers and people who experience psychosis, suggesting a greater degree of social disablement for those who inhabit worlds that are not shared by the cultural mainstream. They highlight the tendency of mental health workers to trivialise or infantilise service users to make sense of this difference, for example, congratulating a woman in her 40s for using the toilet. It is hard to imagine a context outside social care where it would be considered appropriate to do this, yet such remarks are commonplace within it. It would be appropriate in other settings for the recipient of the remark to respond angrily, yet, in a social care setting, it is not uncommon for expressed anger to be translated as challenging or disruptive or as 'hard to engage'. Without thought about the way knowledge is made between people, those spoken of can be named badly, that is reduced to the status of object, or passive recipient of knowledge of them in which disconcerting voices are rendered powerless or, as is often the case, silenced altogether. While it is not as straightforward as this, speakers in the 'know', psychiatrists, community psychiatric nurses (CPNs), social workers etc. are positioned as active speaking subjects with agency and cultural identity. They have the power to name and to 'place' psychosis as out of touch with reality, and to intervene to correct the 'mistake'.

## Learning from contexts – thinking beyond the case notes

We unpack the theme of language, power and action throughout this collection, offering tools for you to make sense of the everyday rituals, rules and practices that make up the *habitus* of your everyday interactions with people that experience psychosis and find ways to develop practice innovation to combat the spirals of hopelessness. One of the learning outcomes of *Psychosis*

*Revisited* was to link these spirals of hopelessness with discrimination in everyday decision-making about people that experience psychosis. Here we want to take this perspective one step further and suggest that the self-perpetuating tendency of them/us habits in service delivery and service use can support a hopeless structural dependency between services and the people that need their help most. In what ways do the continued positioning of people that experience psychosis as 'beyond recovery', or as more hopeless/vulnerable than people experiencing other kinds of mental distress, maintain this structural dependency?

If, as we have suggested, most people want to help, how is this desire best supported in a climate of hopeless everyday decisions? One of the assumptions behind this collection is an ethical responsibility for those in the 'know' to work with an awareness of the ways that language and power can both wound and maintain distress (Butler, 1997b). If the repetition of many tiny discriminatory acts and words becomes a larger trauma or sense of hopelessness over time, Davidson (2008) suggests that an upward spiral of hopeful action is best supported by the repetition of lots of tiny acts and decisions that name people who experience psychosis positively and affirmatively. To build this positive spiral may involve curiosity and a desire to learn about the contexts that may have influenced the sources and maintenance of an individual's distress, and the many contexts that will influence the processes of recovery. The focus on context is thus core to this collection. Knowledge of the person who experiences psychosis usually arrives neatly packaged (placed) within prescribed formats, the risk assessment and the referrals that have normalising and sometimes stigmatising assumptions built into their layout. Often arriving in highly coded language, these contexts of knowing define the parameters of the relationship from the start. As a consequence, other contexts that make up the world of the person who experiences psychosis only come to the fore through these parameters, if they come into the fore at all. For example, a person who experiences psychosis may also be a person who likes music, skateboarding or any number of individual or social activities. Once a person is known through a format, likes, dislikes, hobbies, social roles will be organised and subordinated to it – '*I am a psychotic before I am a person in other contexts*'. We are not arguing for the end of case notes and referrals. The problems of limited information are just as disabling. For example, people who provide care have very little space in statutory documentation and, when workers are pushed for time, tend to fall off the agenda altogether. Without case notes and referrals there would be no possibility of joined up thinking at all in a person's movement through (and hopefully beyond) different services and treatments. Our point is that relating to the other worlds of people that experience psychosis is already difficult enough. It becomes almost impossible if all the information surrounding a person forms a context that, unwittingly, displaces the many contexts that make up their personhood to begin with.

## Why this book?

The primary aim of this collection is to undo some of the dense layers of silence and unwitting discrimination that 'place' people that experience psychosis under hopeless expectations and labels. The aim is to make a space of learning between frontline mental health workers and people that experience psychosis in a way that is already mainstream in most person-centred practices. Each contributor to the collection has participated in the service user-led session of the *Psychosis Revisited* workshop. This session is pivotal to the learning across the two days. Here, we extend this learning opportunity through facilitating a space of expression unconstrained by the usual formats through which the experience of psychosis is placed and known. However, there is no such thing as an unformatted space. As with *Psychosis Revisited*, the service user session is structured through an interview format developed by and for participating speakers. This oral format serves as a point of departure for several of the narratives. To make the transition from an oral to a written medium, the editors organised the collection space on Paul Chadwick's (2006) principle of radical collaboration. This principle is also core to the *Psychosis Revisited* workshop and is based on Carl Roger's (1961) humanistic approach.

Chadwick suggests that therapists often feel '*driven to change minds by their implicit assumptions about how therapy should progress*' (2006). Similarly, frontline mental health workers may often feel driven to change behaviour by their implicit assumptions about how recovery should progress. Chadwick argues for a movement away from engagement with service users to relationship building with them. His approach is easily transferred to ordinary peer relationships and is particularly suited to a recovery-orientated practice that is not willing to define recovery in advance for all participants. It is not at all radical to do this. The radical dimension is supplied by the willingness to collaborate with experiential 'worlds' that may disconcert your own. Chadwick argues, therefore, that it is important not to be judgmental about anti-collaborative attitudes as they arise. Anybody that has not held negative or generalised assumptions about people that experience psychosis (including people that experience psychosis) is simply kidding themselves. Further, many 'illness-saturated environments' have anti-collaborative assumptions built into them from the start; for example, the notion that exploring the meaning a person makes of their experience may be regarded as collusion with delusions and/or reinforcement of them. There is a line between collaborating and colluding. In listening to and exploring 'other worlds', it would be simply dishonest to pretend to inhabit it yourself. However, no learning can take place if workers and people who experience psychosis do not feel safe to explore their respective world views and put down mistaken or oversimplified ones as part of their professional and/or personal development.

A genuinely collaborative relationship combines the openness and curiosity of Socratic questioning, that is dialogue that draws '*attention to material that is currently outside awareness*' (Chadwick, 2006) and supports insight from new experiences to be made sense of within a frame of reference. Facilitating multiple collaborative discovery/recovery journeys thus extends the relationship building of the *Psychosis Revisited* workshops. It brings to the fore the rich tapestry of experience, skill and emotional sensitivity expressed by people often written off as 'beyond recovery' and, not to put too fine a point on it, frequently subjected to the worst forms of stereotyping and negative discrimination in and outside the delivery of mental health services. We aim to show that people who experience psychosis can and do move on, resist labelling and make sense of their lives in ways that may be unusual but certainly do not lack insight into what is going on for them. Within this aim, we make a broader point about the complexity and diversity of lived experience. This, it is shown throughout, is always more than the familiar categories by which diversity is known and audited in mental health, for example, the equal opportunities monitoring that accompanies most job applications. Such categories are indispensable to keeping a big eye on which client groups are represented or under represented in an organisation in relation to local demographic data. However, they say very little about differences between clients from the 'same' category or whose context is made between overlapping categories. Similarly, there is no universal 'mental health worker' although there may be shared professional codes of practice that bind different groups together. In the narratives presented throughout, there are more qualitative differences than similarities between narratives. Yet, on an equal opportunities monitoring form, the differences would appear very slight.

# Collecting the narratives

The editors took a cautious 'hands off' approach to collecting narratives in order to respect the issues of language and power raised above. They did not stop being 'professional people' in this process but decided that making room for contributors to express views that might challenge their own was the first step to the collaborative process described above. Each contributor was asked to write about their experience of recovery and psychosis and offered scribal support on request. It was agreed that no interpretation should be offered by the editors, unless this was asked for by the contributors. Where this was given, it was non-prompting and limited to the request made. Where scribal support was given, narratives were read back for the contributor to edit and no alternative phrasing offered, even though this was asked for on several occasions. Some contributors requested support with grammar, which was given. All contributors were offered payment, which some accepted as recognising their time and some declined because they saw payment as selling their story. Some decided to give their payments to charity.

The core concern throughout was to make room for the contributors to express their worlds *in their own style* through practical support for interpretative agency and a minimal brief to frame this. This involved rolling with the contributors and not putting people under time or word count pressure. These are also ways of framing the content of a narrative, of unwittingly guiding them through organisational pressures and priorities. However, it was not possible to work without any frame at all. We set 10,000 words as an upper limit for each narrative, in the hope that this would not cramp anybody's style unduly. We were given a flexible publishing deadline, which was indispensable for working at the speed people could go. As a result, each narrative is the length it needs to be for each contributor to feel satisfied they have told their story without constraint. Some narratives achieve this in short formats. Some are more extended and one needed extra room. This flexibility on time and space is, we suggest, an essential ingredient in minimising top-down imposition of an unwitting agenda, although it is not possible to avoid this altogether.

The stylistic diversity that emerged through taking a stepped-back approach was very encouraging. Nevertheless, the differences between accounts, lengths, formats etc. may feel a little jarring for readers used to stylistic uniformity in books on mental health. We ask readers to roll with any discomfort this may invoke as part of the process of supporting the interpretative agency of voices that are more used to being interpreted through the formats of people with power over them. If we are to genuinely encounter the diversity between nine people who have experiences that are not culturally mainstream, then it is inevitable that there will be some stylistic discontinuity. Lived experience is messy sometimes. If, as we also assume, readers bring different worlds with them, then these also have different levels of 'mess' tolerance and ways of negotiating it. This can be likened to a preference for sheet music or a preference for jazz. As you read the narratives, it is worth noting your 'mess' tolerance as you will have an opportunity to think about this in the middle of the collection. Here we note that listening to people who are experiencing worlds that are organised very differently to yours can feel disorientating. Learning to work with this disorientation is a core component of effective relationship building. However, it is a process that can only honestly proceed at the pace that it does. To get best use out of this collection, it is worth noting the narratives that jar or disorientate and take the time to ask yourself why that is so. There are no medals for disorientation tolerance. The worker that says this is off my radar is of more help than someone who does not see that the radar is there.

Readers may also find some of the content upsetting. It is now widely recognised that there is a link between childhood trauma, abuse and psychosis in approximately 50% of cases (Read *et al*, 2003), and that is the case in this collection. In discussion of this dimension of the narratives, it was agreed that nobody had told their story for shock value or to make others feel bad. There are also accounts of treatment that fall very short of the standards of care that all people should expect from 21st century health services. Some are more recent than others but all point to serious gaps in understanding and unwillingness to listen to people that experience psychosis. The contributors that debated this point argued that for those for whom the lived experience has been upsetting, nothing was to be gained by pretending otherwise. However, everybody wanted their experience to be both constructive and instrumental in making a difference in current practice and nobody wanted to engage in 'service bashing'. The contributors were united in the common aim of 'telling it like it was', there is no way round the fact that experiences of psychosis can be disturbing and handing over practice points that either were helpful or would be helpful if they lived through their experiences again. If you are an experienced mental health worker, it is likely that you will have already heard similar or more disconcerting accounts. If you are a new mental health worker, the collection gives you the opportunity to acclimatise yourself, in the relatively safe world of text, to the kinds of narratives you might encounter in the work place. If you are a person that experiences psychosis, the narratives offer a rich resource to affirm and support your recovery process. Each narrative has been through a dark time and found a way through in their recovery pathway. Nevertheless, as with the *Psychosis Revisited* workshops, dark and difficult times are described. Taking the narratives out of the bounded space of the interview format also involves consideration of their impact on an audience we have not met, some of whom may have lived experience or may be experiencing distress. There is no way round this. Our recommendation is that if you are feeling very fragile and vulnerable at the moment, then now might not be the best time to hear about the fragilities and vulnerabilities of others. If this is so, we hope you shelve us for a later date.

Given the sensitivity of these themes, the question of disclosure has been extensively discussed throughout the collection process. There is a big difference between writing a story down in private, or in a one-to-one setting and letting it go out into the world. As stated above, all contributors had experience of telling their stories with an audience in a workshop setting. However, this is a bounded space with rules of confidentiality and safe questioning procedures (see Hayward *et al*, 2005 for an example of such procedures). Signing your name to a text that could be read by anybody gives up the protection of this bounded space and could lead to an increased sense of vulnerability. To keep people and their families feeling safe, contributors were offered the choice to remain anonymous. Two meetings were arranged for participating authors to read each others' narratives and acclimatise themselves to the exposure. Contributors were asked to feedback their interpretations of each other's work in a whole group setting and to consider how they would feel if a stranger asked an invasive or unexpected question, or interpreted them in a way they did not recognise or appreciate. For those that chose not to be anonymous, themes such as potential increase in stigmatised relations, from potential employers, for example, or from their local communities were discussed. Contributors were offered the opportunity to take back their narratives or change them if they felt uncomfortable in this process and to collectively own the project. This space was well used. Some contributors made changes to their narratives and one took the opportunity to withdraw. Contributors also used the space to edit the editors and make arrangements for further proofing and collective editing of the text.

Voicing Psychotic Experiences: A reconsideration of recovery and diversity

# How to use this book

The collection of narratives offered here, presents a range of descriptions of what has been helpful and unhelpful to people who experience psychosis, what has supported their recovery and some of the obstacles that have been encountered. No narrative arrives innocent of language and power. The best that can be achieved is to make these relations explicit. This book includes no voices from people from ethnic minorities, gay, bi and lesbian identities or from members from communities with physical disabilities. This is, in part, due to the largely white conservative community from which *Psychosis Revisited* emerged. It may also say something about the way the workshop has consistently been presented by people that experience psychosis but have not experienced a great deal of discrimination on other grounds. There is also only one contribution from the perspective of a person who is a caregiver. It was decided that it would be wholly tokenistic to seek out contributors to fill these gaps. Nevertheless, it is important to identify them as gaps in our understanding that we hope will be inhabited by readers from a wider spectrum of experience.

Each writer holds a view about what their experience of psychosis means and what recovery is. Each perspective contains a set of core beliefs, ranging through medical, pragmatic, social, psychological and spiritual interpretations of psychosis and recovery. There is no sense in which any narrative is valued as of more intrinsic worth than another. However, we also wish to extend the principle of radical collaboration to readers. You will also bring core beliefs, skills and different interpretative frameworks to the sense that is made of each contribution. It is our hope that dialogue with the narratives will give you practical tips for talking with and listening to people that experience psychosis and some ideas about how you can best support a range of recovery journeys and/or your own. To make best use of this book, it is recommended that you start your journey by filling in the questionnaire at the end of this section. In this way, the collection can be read as a supplement to *Psychosis Revisited*, enabling key issues from the workshop to be fleshed out through the lived experience of the people who played a significant part in making the training manual what it is. We never step in the same river twice. The act of writing is also an act of reflection on the core assumptions that frame our relationships to each other. The act of facilitating dialogue between many overlapping worlds is an opportunity for readers to think about their core assumptions about psychosis and recovery. Are we talking about an illness to be cured or different realities to be lived with? We want to provoke thought about where you stand in your world and how you and your organisation facilitate dialogue with worlds substantially different from your own. Most importantly, we want you to own feelings of negativity and/or anxiety that may be invoked when working with a person who experiences psychosis. It is not a bad thing to experience these, but it may not be helpful to operate out of them unconsciously. There is pause for thought about these issues in the middle of the collection, unpacking radical collaboration further and offering Barry Mason's framework of 'safe uncertainty' (1993) to support this process. These frameworks encourage you to take a step back from habitual 'unsafe certainty' that supports risk adverse practices and to think about ways of building effective ordinary relationships with people that experience psychosis. The collection thus stands on its own as an aid to reflect on professional development for frontline mental health workers and aims to reach out and offer encouragement to people whose experiences of psychosis remain unvoiced. It is fitting and timely, therefore, that the narratives should take centre stage.

## Where am I now?

1   Who am I? Write a short description of your world. This can include, but is not limited to, personal qualities; experience; skills; values; cultural/social identity; likes and dislikes; friends; relationships etc.

2   Which of the above do you believe could be best developed to support communication with people whose world may be very different from your own?

3   Which of the above do you believe is least supportive of communication with people whose world may be very different from your own?

4a  List the first three words that come to mind when you hear the word psychosis.
4b  Do these words express positive or negative expectations about people who experience psychosis?

5   Can you think of any habits of speech or action in your workplace that is optimistic about people that experience psychosis?

6   Can you think of any habits of speech or action that is pessimistic about people that experience psychosis in your workplace?

7   How do you feel when a person talks to you about an idea or thought they have, which you think is unusual?

8a  Have you had any experiences of talking with and listening to people that experience psychosis and who have been particularly helpful to your understanding of them?
8b  If so, what was helpful about it?

9a  Have you had any experiences of talking with and listening to people that experience psychosis and who have been particularly difficult and/or obstructive of your understanding of them?
9b  If so, what was difficult about it?

10  What are the views and attitudes of your colleagues and/or friends about talking and listening to people about their unusual experiences?

# References

Anthony WA (1993) Recovery from mental illness: The guiding vision of the mental health service system in the 1990s. *Pyschosocial Rehabilitation Journal* **16** 11–23a.

Basset T, Hayward M, Chandler R, Blank A, Cooke A & Read J (2007) *Psychosis Revisited: A recovery based workshop for mental health workers, service users and carers.* Brighton: Pavilion.

British Psychological Society (2000) *Understanding Mental Illness: Recent advances in understanding mental illness and psychotic experiences.* Leicester: BPS.

Butler J (1997a) *Excitable Speech: A politics of the performative.* New York: Routledge.

Butler J (1997b) *The Psychic Life of Power: Theories of subjection.* California: Stanford University Press.

Chadwick P (2006) *Person-Based Cognitive Therapy for Distressing Psychosis.* Chichester: Wiley.

Davidson L (2008) *Researching the Evaluation of Recovery Programmes.* Paper presented at the Centre for Mental Health Recovery Research Seminar, University of Hertfordshire.

Glover H (2008) *Creating environments that are facilitative of individual recovery processes.* Unpublished manuscript. Available from authors on request.

Harrison G, Hopper K, Craig T, Laska E, Siegel C, Wanderling J, Dube KC, Ganev K, Giel R, An Der Heiden W, Holmberg SK, Janca A, Lee PWH, Leon CA, Malhotra S, Marsella AJ, Nakane T, Sartorius N, Shen Y, Skoda C, Thata R, Tsirkin SJ, Varma VK, Walsh D & Wiersma D (2001) Recovery from Psychotic Illness. A 15 and 25 year follow up study. *British Journal of Psychiatry* **178** 505–517.

Hayward M, West S, Green M & Blank A (2005) Service innovations: service user involvement in training. *Psychiatric Bulletin* **29** 428–430.

Hayward M & Slade M (2008) Getting better … who decides? *The Psychologist* **21** 198–200.

Houghton P, Shaw B, Hayward M & West S (2006) Psychosis revisited: taking a collaborative look at psychosis. *Mental Health Practice* **9** 40–43.

Hughes R, Hayward M & Finlay WML (2008) Patients' perception of the impact of involuntary inpatient care on self, relationships and recovery. *Journal of Mental Health.* **18** (2) 152-160.

Mason B (1993) Towards positions of safe uncertainty. *Human Systems: The Journal of Systems Consultation and Management* **4** 198–200.

National Institute for Mental Health England (2004) *Emerging Best Practices in Mental Health Recovery* [online]. Available at: http://www.nimhe.csip.org.uk/silo/files/mentalhealthrecoverypdf.pdf (last accessed April 2009).

Perkins R & Dilks S (1992) Worlds apart: working with severely socially disabled people. *Journal of Mental Health* **1** 3–17.

Read J, Agar K, Argyle N & Aderhold V (2003) Sexual and physical abuse during childhood and adulthood as predictors of hallucinations, delusions and thought disorder. *Psychology and Psychotherapy: Theory, research and practice* **76** 1–23.

Repper J & Perkins R (2003) *Social Inclusion and Recovery: A model for mental health Practice.* London: Baillière Tindal.

Rogers C (1961) *On Becoming a Person.* Constable: London.

Shepherd G, Boardman J & Slade M (2008) *Making Recovery a Reality.* London: Sainsbury Centre for Mental Health.

Slade M & Hayward M (2007) Recovery, psychosis and psychiatry: research is better than rhetoric. *Acta Psychiatrica Scandinavia* **116** 81–83.

# Chapter 1

# Shirley's legs

Steven West

As far as recovery goes, you do not recover from psychosis, you learn to manage it, hopefully. This is how psychosis has affected me.

## My history

I was born in 1959 at home. My father delivered me. It was in a village called Lowfield Heath at the end of Gatwick airport runway. I was the middle son of a family of six children. My eldest brother lived in an institution because he suffered from hydrocephalous. In 1963, we moved to a town called Burgess Hill in West Sussex where I went to school. I was sexually abused three times in my life at age six, 10 and 15 but not by a family member. I was teased sometimes at school and resorted to violence in answer to this issue. When I started senior school, I decided that I would use violence if anybody teased me any more; the teasing subsided. I started playing truant in my first year at senior school and my behaviour was not good in class. When I did attend, I attended more detentions than I care to remember. Sadly, I would have achieved the progress prize in my class but it was not awarded to me because I played truant.

In my second year at senior school, my behaviour improved although my academic achievements were still very low. I could not read properly or spell very well, and I used to copy the teacher's information, letter for letter off the blackboard. We now know there is dyslexia in the family and although I've never been tested for it, there is a probability that I suffer with it. At the ages of 12 and 14, I suffered two episodes of depression that were not diagnosed at the time, but I later recognised as periods of illness. In the third year of senior school, I became friendly with a girl. Although my attendance was now regular, the work towards my exams was really going nowhere. In the fifth year at school, some truancy was occurring. I had thoughts about becoming a labourer because this did not involve reading and writing and my school work was very patchy. One day, early in my last year at school, I had an argument with a teacher who had previously said nasty things to me. I walked across the field about 200 yards from him and produced a penknife, and yelled abuse at him. I walked towards him gathering the crowd along the way, as the teacher was very unpopular. I didn't attack the teacher and walked out of school instead. Another teacher, for whom I and most other pupils in the school had high regard, came to speak to me but I ran away.

The following day I was suspended for a week and in that week my father and I went to see the teacher I respected. He asked me if I wanted to continue at the school with my exams, to which I said no, and he said to my father that it might be better if Steven leaves.

I got a job within a week or so of leaving school at an engineering factory. The work was hard and the pay was miniscule. I was dismissed from the job for not being able to keep up. I then, unwisely, got a labouring job with the water company. This was 1976, in the hottest summer on record, and the ground was like iron to dig. I was there a few months and was dismissed from that job because the work was too physically demanding. I had a part-time job after that in a laminating factory for four or five weeks. At the end of the year, I got another full-time job on a building site as an aide to the manager and doing bits of labouring work. After a row with the deputy manager, I was sacked for swearing at him in front of his manager. After several months of unemployment, I got in trouble with the law for the first time, being drunk and disorderly and for carrying an offensive weapon. I was given probation for this – then two or three months later, my friend and I broke into the cinema where I had a part-time job. I was given community service for that offence.

A couple of months later I was seen by the police carrying a metal implement and arrested. For this offence, I was given three months in a detention centre, which was run a little like the army. I hated my time there because some of the boys intimidated me. On my release, I thought I would never commit another offence. I worked at a chain-making factory making jewellery after leaving the detention centre. Still on probation, I worked there for about 15 months and left to work at a paint spraying, packing and case-making freight forwarding company in Crawley. This doubled my wages. On celebrating my new job, friends and I went to Brighton to have a drink. We missed the last train home and me and one of my friends stole a car. We took it to London and were chased by the police, arrested and charged with taking and driving away a vehicle. I believe I was fined. I worked at the paint spraying firm for about eight months then left the job to go grape picking in France. I thought it was all going to be horse and cart and romantic, but it was hard work and tractors. Never saw a horse while I was out there but I met some nice people. I returned to England around November, which was the coldest winter in a hundred years and I was under canvas! I returned home and a few months later I took my sister's car out and smashed it up because I hadn't learned to drive. I was kicked out of the family home. I went to Brighton and attempted to steal another car. I was thwarted by the owner, arrested by the police and held on remand in prison by the courts. I came off of remand in prison and was put on probation. I lodged at my friend's house up until my first admission to hospital in 1983.

## Hospital

On admission to hospital, I recognised the psychiatrist as I had seen him once for a court assessment some time earlier. Also one of my sister's friends had seen this doctor and had a given a poor report of his performance. Nevertheless, I was tearful and frightened when he asked me would I come into the hospital as a voluntary patient. The unit was built in the early 60s and the ward was downstairs from where we were speaking. When saying yes, I imagined that the ward would be like a Victorian asylum. While in need of a lick of paint here and there, the architecture was definitely 60s. When I went downstairs, the first thing I had to do was change into pyjamas, bathrobe and some slippers. I did not notice at the time where my clothes had gone. My father had been a sergeant in the Royal Air Force and my mother was also in the Air Force after the war. My father went on to become an electronics engineer working at Gatwick. He was interested in UFOs and paranormal phenomena. Both my parents were Christians and we had to go to church till the age of 16, then we had the choice. I chose not to go at 16. We had discussed UFOs and paranormal phenomena many times, which fascinated me. We also discussed the Second World War a lot. I found myself slipping from reality after a day or two in hospital. One of the patients liked wearing paramilitary clothes and I thought he was a policeman. One of the reasons I worried about whether the police were there was because I had been smoking cannabis on and off since 1980 prior to my admission to hospital.

Weeks literally turned into months. For the first three months, I was always in the presence of a nurse or a student nurse. I constantly tried to run away and was brought back to the psychiatric ward and on one occasion by a neurological surgeon in his car from the hospital adjacent. One day, I escaped at night and was brought back by the police. They were really nice and I did not feel threatened by them. However, amidst all this time a delusion started in which I somehow was important to aliens. There were good and bad aliens. Hitler was in one UFO and there was a good ship that had tried to save me. Also, I imagined that there was witchcraft going on, and as if that wasn't enough that the Mafia knew of my importance to the aliens and were looking to exploit the situation in their favour! I also imagined that Mrs Thatcher had dispatched the SAS to intercept me before getting into a good or bad alien ship. My thought processes where totally illogical as a stand off scenario seemed to exist for several weeks with me just remaining where I was in hospital. Slowly, as I started to interact with the art therapy, music therapy, cooking classes, tennis, swimming and quizzes, the delusions began to fade and I could no longer hang on to my imagined sense of importance although it would have been nice to hang on to it. Also, whilst interacting with the students, male and female I noticed that they lived lives outside of petty crime, unemployment and cannabis and I thought I could change too. After spending five months in total at the hospital, I was discharged.

On discharge, it was suggested to me that I could be either a manic depressive or a paranoid schizophrenic. They opted to treat me as a paranoid schizophrenic. The aftercare from the acute unit was based in the grounds of a large psychiatric hospital. I attended an industrial therapy unit where I packed screws and rawlplugs into little polythene bags for about 18 months. Somewhere in that period of time, I was sent to a rehabilitation or work centre in Croydon. I was chosen to do a six-month capstan setter operator course, which I tried about two months later, but I could not read either the micrometer or the ruler to set the machine properly, so I left the course and returned to the industrial therapy unit. This was because the medication I was on was affecting my eyesight. At this time, the unit changed to a crafts and outside work for the council (bridle-paths and wooden bridges). I then got a job in the district laundry, based at the main psychiatric hospital, which did my confidence no good. Also that year, I moved into a group home as I had been living with my parents since leaving hospital. All went well then and I moved jobs after 18 months to work at Gatwick Airport as an aircraft cleaner, which meant my wages about doubled again.

After about a year, I had a motorcycle accident in which I was off work for several weeks. A paranoid thought occurred to me that it may have been the driver deliberately trying to kill me. Several weeks later, I became unwell but was unable to convince the doctor that I was ill. During this bout of illness, I broke into the call-box telephone at the group home to get money to run away. I was never charged with the crime but lost my place in the group home – the whole bout of illness was outside hospital care. After a year's unemployment, I got a job packing and case-making in a freight forwarding firm. I told them at my interview about my mental illness and they still employed me. I worked there for about 15 months before becoming unwell. When I told my manager that I had been to the GP about my mental anxiety he 'ummed' and 'ahhed' but the deputy manager reminded my boss about what I had said at interview. Then they were ok with it. I was taken to hospital after my friends called the police for my safety. I was admitted by the ward sister whom had been a student in 1983 on the ward where I was staying. My new consultant rediagnosed me as having bipolar manic depression disorder, and said to me that 'we' (not him on his own) were going to manage the illness. After about three and a half months, I was discharged from hospital and started to attend the Stead Resource Centre, which was the new version of the old IT workshop.

## Shirley (my wife) – new hope

After a few months, the manager of Stead informed me that there was a part-time cleaning job at a care home – was I interested? Yes, I said! It was at the care home a year later that I met my future wife after being asked by her friend if I liked to take her out on her birthday. We talked on that first date and she told me she suffered with multiple sclerosis and I told her that I had mental health issues. We dated for two months and she then moved into the flat where I lived. On New Year's Eve of that winter, I proposed to her as the bells of Big Ben were ringing in the New Year. She left me for nine dongs before saying yes! We married in August of 1993 and she gave me a son we named Ryan in May of 1994. This time, I was working as a driver for a cleaning company, having passed my driving test two days before my son was born. I, at this time, felt emotionally complete and my confidence was very high.

About the same time as I met Shirley, I became involved with the consumer group, which was a group of people that use services and were carers of people that use services, and which tried to monitor the psychiatric unit I had been attending. We moved from the flat to stay with Shirley's parents as Shirley was buying half the house with them. This went well at first, but then I became unwell again and was admitted to hospital in 1996. It seemed to me that this was one of my blackest admissions, although I made two friends whom I'm still friendly with today. Shirley and Ryan moved to a two bedroom flat after giving up the mortgage because we needed space as a married couple on my return from hospital. On discharge, the same consultant who diagnosed me with bipolar suggested that I was unfit for full-time work. I got a part-time job driving for a drop-in club in Haywards Heath for people with mental health issues. I also became involved a couple of years later with volunteer advocacy for Mind, which I thoroughly enjoyed. In 1999, I joined the Capital project (clients and professionals in training and learning).

In 2003, I was sectioned for the first time whilst in an admission to an acute unit. The same fears had arisen with the SAS being out to get me. I ran from the unit across the road to a petrol station and poured petrol over myself and threatened to light a lighter. Thank God for the security guard from the hospital who rugby tackled me and prevented me from possible death. I was sectioned under the Mental Health Act and taken to Crawley Police Station. My doctor spent 20 minutes on the phone convincing the police psychiatrist that he could care for me in our local unit rather than a forensic unit, which he did and I was discharged six weeks later. I have found that I believe we are mind, body and spirit. After leaving hospital in 1984, I started to attend Haywards Heath Baptist Church. I was baptised in 1987 and I found that spiritual balance speeds recovery of psychosis providing you take the tablets, sleep and eat.
In 2002, Shirley's health began to get worse and she needed to be in a wheelchair for outside

activities. Shirley was the thinker and the planner and I was physically fit. We always used to joke about this, saying I was Shirley's legs and Shirley was my brain. We functioned really well as a couple. Around the flat, she could get by with her tri-walker – the best £100 I ever spent. This aid gave her a bit of freedom for about a year. In late 2003, Shirley lost the use of her legs entirely and had to be hoisted in and out of a wheelchair. At this point in time, we were given the help of carers to get Shirley up in the morning and put her to bed at night. This went on with things getting worse and worse until 2007 when Shirley became bed bound. Shirley always, and even at this stage, had an active input with my community psychiatric nurse (CPN) (Chris Riggs) whom I had known as a student in 1983, and had become my CPN in 1991. Between the three of us, we had managed my illness and reduced the risk of further illness as much as possible. Shirley sadly passed away in September 2007.

## Shirley, me and recovery

Shirley always made me feel complete. Having given me a fine son and a tender heart, I can go on now because I know she is no longer suffering. I don't think I will be ill because I know when to ask for help since Shirley has passed away. I have found that continuity of care, a loving family and acceptance of a cyclical illness enables me to keep my illness in check. I received talking therapy for over five years with one counsellor – who sadly died. The counselling stopped and I received replacement counselling for a further year. I found both counsellors very helpful. Although the underlying issues hadn't gone away, I learned to manage and cope with them. I've enjoyed and found therapeutic benefit as a service user contributor to the *Psychosis Revisited* workshop. I have been participating for six years and hope to continue with this.

As far as the meds are concerned, I was overmedicated in the early 80s but I find that the modern drugs are more precise and subtle in application. I have found over the years that taking medication is one way to mange my illness. On three or four occasions, when feeling well, I've tested this and come off my medication thinking I did not need it. The emotions come into play because I am taking medication, I am labelled. After each occasion of withdrawal and denial of my illness, I became ill and came down with a big bump! I find that taking medication reduces the amount of admissions to hospital and their severity. Also, I find that taking medication means that there isn't a cliff to fall off of (metaphorically speaking) when becoming unwell. I now take my medication regularly as part of my daily routine without hesitation. I find the meds help me keep going. Knowing when to ask for help and living a balanced lifestyle maximises the possibility of me remaining well.

Currently, I have started adult education, doing basic English, as well as one morning a week doing voluntary work for Age Concern. I intend and hope to get my European Computing Driving License after my English and to return to work under the permitted work scheme in the next couple of years.

### Some thoughts on good practice
- Continuity of care (same people)
- Consistency in approach (across different people)
- Collaborating in management of my illness
- High calibre of reciprocal communication
- Having time and being patient

What the future holds I cannot tell, but boldly I move forward.

# Chapter 2

# Discovering me

Becky Shaw

Can I emphasise the positive experience of writing for the book and writing in general. Other people I know have expressed similar positive feelings when they have written their experiences down.

## About me

Having experienced psychosis since I was very little, I should be an expert now on how to cope with hearing voices. I know what to do when the hallucinations are very distressing, although this doesn't always mean I can cope. You see, recovery for me is not about getting rid of the distressing hallucinations and other disabling symptoms of having mental health difficulties, no, recovery for me has been to realise that, although I have my difficulties, I can still lead a normal, full and meaningful life to the best of my abilities. You would not expect someone who is in a wheelchair, who doctors expect never to walk again, to suddenly be able to walk, but this does not mean they cannot also lead a full and meaningful life. Accepting that I may never get rid of these symptoms and learning instead to adapt and live with them has been for me part of the process of recovery.

The other thing I have had to accept is that not everyone in the world will like me for who I am and accept the difficulties I face; I know now that it should not stop me from being open about my mental health with others, even with this fear of rejection. People get rejected all the time for many reasons and it can be hard sometimes to face the fact that not everyone is going to like you as a person. I have accepted that. It is great that we are all unique individuals and a diverse species. It is what makes us human and gives us strength. Because I no longer fear being open, I am not as paranoid about people finding out about my mental health difficulties. I have also found that it wasn't as bad as I expected and that being open has in fact intrigued people and helped them to also open up about themselves. I still get some people who don't want to know and some who are prejudiced, but letting people get to know me first and being open has gone some way to dismissing the myths surrounding mental health problems.

Accepting me for who I am also helped me when I became visually impaired five years ago. I used the very same philosophy of adaptation and acceptance, and the belief that I could live a full and meaningful life, just like I have done with my mental health difficulties. However, I have had to face many battles and have jumped many hurdles to get to where I am today. At the moment I am happy with who I am, but it has not always been that way. I am hoping that by telling my story others can learn from my experiences and realise that there is always light at the end of the tunnel.

## The early years

As a child hearing voices, especially one male voice that others could not hear, was a part of my life. It was not upsetting hearing him talk. He was, in fact, a much needed companion and friend and still is today. He is still as very real as anyone out there. He was the sort of friend you can have a laugh with, argue and debate with or be still with. He was a companion who would talk endlessly sometimes and at other times not at all, but I would still talk back and know he was listening. He was my only true friend and was always blunt, to the point, and honest about life.

I learnt very early on that it was not acceptable to hear things others couldn't and therefore kept 'him' to myself. I would chat to him and people would stare at me and talk about me and my strange ways. I spent most of the time on my own out walking with my dog, or in my room and had very few friends. As a child, attending school for the first time is always a shock to the system but for me it seemed a hurdle that was just too big. I would come home from school and sit and scream. I could not talk to my parents about the constant bullying. I would talk to the voices, especially him, and because I was always lost in my own world other children would either stay away from me or bully me. The stress of the bullying caused the voices to become more negative, as a reflection of the inner turmoil I was experiencing. I do not know whether the voice hearing or the bullying was making things worse for me; probably the confusion and the conflict between the two? The voices became very negative and angry with me and the other children.

It was hard going from a safe protected world of childhood innocence, wrapped in cotton wool by my parents, to a school where I was not only bullied but, for a short time, physically abused as well. I locked these traumatic memories of childhood down deep inside and learnt to suppress all of my emotions. I was scared that if I dared to cry, I would not be able to contain the outpouring of emotions. I knew that, by doing this, I was making myself ill but I did not know at the time how much worse it would get. The voices had now become distressing, especially after the period of physical abuse; they started to harass me and bully me themselves. They became angry and abusive in manner and they questioned my every action, judging everything I did or thought. I know now that they had fed on the traumatic experiences buried deep down inside me. They revealed their disgust of me and paranoid delusions started to set in.

I was always paranoid about what other people were thinking of me and whether they hated or liked me, and I was constantly evaluating and analysing people and situations. I still do this today, but as a child I could not control it and the paranoia turned into delusions of which I could not make sense. However, it was my constant searching to make sense of them and situations and people that made them worse. A lot of the time there is no clear answer and you cannot analyse someone else's inner private thoughts.

I was only 12 at this point in time and had started at secondary school. At first I managed, but then at 15 I was raped, and again I blocked out the distress this caused, telling no one of the event, not even my parents. Parents and teachers knew something was wrong but they didn't know what and when they dared to ask I just recoiled. How could I explain something that I did not understand myself? Children at my school no longer talked to me and I became more and more isolated, perpetuating the problems. Again I was bullied, not physically this time but mentally, and for me this was worse.

I went to university to study teaching and science. I had by now found other more destructive coping mechanisms including excessive use of alcohol, which I used to block out the hurt and to get to sleep. I also self-harmed by cutting my arms and legs, which gave me a great sense of relief. At the end of the third year I had become so isolated in my flat that I could no longer venture out. I would not let anyone in and the delusions had overtaken me.

## First access to services

A friend became so worried that they eventually phoned my parents who collected me and took me home to a GP. It wasn't long before I was hospitalised, drugged up to the eyeballs with medication and trapped in the mental health system. The first professional person I agreed to talk to about my difficulties was a nurse at the GP surgery who I had known for many years. It was extremely hard. I did not want to admit I was depressed but as soon as I said that I was, I shed my first tear in over six years. A problem shared might not be quite a problem halved but it was a relief for someone else to know and also a relief that I had finally admitted to myself that I needed help. I still did not talk about any of the psychotic experiences I was getting, including tactile and taste hallucinations, or paranoia, as I did not know how to explain these strange experiences. However, it was the first time that I admitted that I self-harmed.

The nurse took the time to listen to me and when I had finished she asked whether I thought I could see a doctor at the surgery, as there was help out there for the difficulties I was experiencing. She did not judge or jump to conclusions; all she did was care about me, which shone through her manner, her voice and every word she spoke. Going to the doctor at the surgery was different though. I did not feel safe or able to open up properly at all, but because the nurse had already spoken to him he knew what was going on with me. Medication was the first thing suggested, although I mentioned time and time again that I just needed someone to talk with. Eventually, I reluctantly agreed to take the antidepressants. I was also referred to the local mental health team and assigned a care co-ordinator and psychiatrist.

It would be a further six years before I received the talking therapy that I had first asked for from the GP, and it was only after receiving this talking therapy that I began to turn the tide of depression towards recovery. I discovered along the way that for me, medication had never been the whole answer. I still take some medication but in smaller doses, mainly because I cannot stop some due to the withdrawal effects. After taking multiple medications for over 12 years at high doses, it is very hard to withdraw, like any drug, licit or illicit.

## The voice-hearing experience

Before I can explain how I used to cope and how I cope now, I need to explain in more detail what it is like for someone to hear voices that other people cannot hear. People who do not experience hearing voices tend to think it must be like the internal voice we all get but outside your head, but this is not so. The voices I have always experienced are clear and human and although quiet or small they are very much real. They also all have individual personalities and characters, just as the male voice 'him' (that I still hear today) that I grew up with. He is grumpy and moody, swinging from happy to sad, to angry and back again. I can envisage what he would look like in the flesh. He would be middle aged, salt and pepper pot wiry hair and stressed with life, with a very short fuse and temper. Other voices I have heard might also be real people in my life. I sometimes hear my friends talk about me in another room, and when I go in to talk to them they will not even be there, they will be upstairs. The voices I hear come in all sorts of guises. A lot of the time on buses I will hear one person start to talk about me and even mention my name. At the end of the bus journey everyone will have talked about me at some point. For a long time I could not catch buses or even go out of the house because it caused me to have panic attacks.

Hearing things that others cannot hear is not limited to just hearing people talk. I sometimes hear a child crying in the walls of a house where I live. I hear noises like bumps, crashes and even music. These sounds are clear as a bell, as if they are in the room or just next door. It is hard sometimes to distinguish what is real from what is not real. Are the neighbours talking over the fence? Is it a hallucination? Is it real? It helps if someone I trust can also tell me if they are real or not. I can also tell if they are not real if the voices I am hearing are extremely negative and personal towards me, or if the person is saying something they would not usually say or believe. Sometimes it is easier to know the difference – for example, if I am hearing a child crying in the walls of my house, I am usually able to know that this is a hallucination. However, sometimes it does become extremely hard to know the difference between a real voice/experience and a hallucination.

I can usually tell when I am deteriorating if I can no longer distinguish which of my experiences are real and which are not. It becomes even harder when I cannot check out with someone I trust what is real and what is not. It is at this point that the hallucinations spiral out of control and the delusions kick in. It is very real and at times very frightening, and also confusing.

## What helps me to cope?

When the delusions have set in and I believe that the voice and associated delusions are real, this is the point where I have crashed and need help quickly. I prevent things from spiralling to this point by the coping strategies I have in place. Coping strategies might include harmful and even dangerous acts eg. self-harming by cutting, drinking or eating toxic substances, bingeing and purging etc. but they do help. Coping strategies also include positive ways of coping too, for example:

- Cleaning
- Hoovering
- Writing
- Listening to music
- Listening to talking books
- Relaxation
- Lavender oil
- Massage
- Acupuncture

- Friends and family
- Checking out with a friend what is real and what is not
- Humming and singing to myself
- Talking back to the voices
- Talking with people I trust about the voices
- Being open about my mental health

However, one of my main strategies is to keep busy and active, and includes doing things like writing, teaching, research and undertaking my degree. The latter things must be undertaken in moderation and at my own pace.

All of the coping mechanisms I have act as a release of built up tension, emotion and thought. I never used to be aware that things were building up inside of me. I am now more aware than I have ever been and I think this is why I consider myself to be at a certain level of recovery. I can recognise the signs when I am stressed, down in mood or hyperactive and then I can do something about it. I have also learnt to use more of the positive coping strategies I have mentioned, although I sometimes still use the more destructive ones when I really need them.

Self-harm is often associated with being suicidal but they are very different. I have experienced both but the easy way to explain the difference is that self-harm is used to avoid getting worse and is used by me and other people to cope, survive and to live. When I felt suicidal I no longer wanted to live; it was my way of escaping the pain and the hurt and even if there was nothing in the afterlife this would have been better than living. So, another part of my recovery is that I want to live because I have something to live for, I have meaning and purpose and love in my life.

## Learning to accept me

It has been a rollercoaster of a journey in getting to where I am today. I have had to fight discrimination and stigma caused by being labelled as 'mentally ill'. I have had to overcome my own fears about what people think about me as a person and face the fact that a lot of people will not want to know me. However, the biggest hurdle for me has been to learn to accept myself for who I am with all my faults and learn to express my emotions in order to be able to lead an independent life. This process has not been easy. It has taken me 12 years since leaving university with my parents to get to where I am today and I still need to work hard at it everyday. It has been a process of discovery towards recovery. Some days are still harder than others. I spend some days in bed, others in the house and garden, and sometimes I feel able to go out and about and meet people. On other days I do some voluntary work, which enables me to have a sense of self-worth. Most of this voluntary work involves helping others who also have mental health difficulties and who are also finding their path along their journey of discovery. I have learned not to beat myself up for the days I am unable to get out and need to rest. I have also learned many coping strategies for the hallucinations, delusions, depression and other psychotic experiences.

So what has helped me to learn all this? My peers, others who do, or have previously experienced mental health distress have helped tremendously. The peer support group I started 15 years ago has helped me more than it has helped others, although they would argue with me about that. It also helped seeing a psychologist for two years. He gave me the time and space to work through the emotions of the past before helping me to look at the future. Although he was a psychologist, he was not focused on techniques and fancy methods of intervention or therapy. He was himself and accepted me for myself. He got to know me as an individual and developed a relationship where I could be entirely open and felt safe to explore the issues that I needed to work through. I have continued this process through other methods like writing, teaching and reflecting.

## Teaching and the *Psychosis Revisited* workshops

There are other things I have been involved in through my voluntary work that have also helped me. Using my experience to help others, whether it has been through running my peer support group through teaching, conducting research or even writing this chapter, has helped me to look at my life with different eyes, feel valued and meet and make friends. One of the training sessions I was involved in from the beginning was the *Psychosis Revisited* two-day workshops. I worked on these workshops with my co-peer trainers who were a mix of people and professionals, including others who had experienced mental health distress, psychologists and a mental health nurse. We worked as a team where I was not patronised or labelled but where I was a true member of the team. I was and still am an equal. This was a milestone in my recovery process as I suddenly realised that I am as valuable as anyone else on this planet. The way I had been labelled by society and by mental health professionals, and their treatment of me and attitudes towards me, had effectively labelled me as a second-class citizen. Before this time, I had always accepted my second-class citizen status to be true.

*Psychosis Revisited* training not only helped in my recovery process by making me see myself as someone who is equal, valued and respected but also by being challenged by the other trainers, as equally as I challenged them. The relationship, between me and my co-trainers, was a true partnership, not tokenistic and not patronising or over protective. They did not pretend to know what psychosis was like or that they had the answers, and as I learnt from them they also learnt from me. For me and the psychologists, the way we worked as a team of trainers was refreshing.

I do not know whether it was because of the psychologists' views or because of the *Psychosis Revisited* training approach, perhaps both, that made sense to me and rang true within me, but it just worked. I wanted to be involved within the whole of the training and not just be rolled out as a subject to be presented in the session on 'service user perspectives', as the manual suggested. This was immediately fine with my colleagues and yes, they were and still are colleagues who are on an equal footing as trainers together, all trying to achieve the same aims.

We saw that the aims of the *Psychosis Revisited* training were to encourage a change in the attitudes and behaviour of mental health staff through education, information and from first-hand experience given to them from someone who had used the service. Over the two days, space was given to discuss and reflect on practice. During the training I was treated as an equal for the first time in my life. The mental health services may still talk down to me but can't take away my new found sense of self, and I have a right to be heard and to be understood. I would not have gained this without being involved in the *Psychosis Revisited* workshop. I have a lot to thank for the people, my co-trainers and that period of time. It was a very important step in my discovery working my way towards recovery.

# Discrimination

Society, however, does not treat me or anyone who has a mental health difficulty as an equal. I went from having a reasonable life with a few friends, not many but enough, a place of my own and a future career where people respected me as much as I respected them and treated me as an equal. However, as soon as I was labelled mentally ill people treated me differently. Society looked down on me either as a burden, something to be afraid of or as something to be sorry for. You might at this point say, 'Yes, but you were paranoid and unwell and you only say this because you were mentally ill', but no, it is very much real. I will give some examples:

- people would cross the road to avoid me
- I have been called 'psycho' and 'nutter'
- friends have had graffiti on their walls
- I have been attacked.

If you think these must be one-off experiences, I will confirm they are not. Incidents like this are just not talked about; they go unseen. Even the media fuel the fire and new government legislation seeks to lock us away, contain us and control us even though we are no more of a danger than anyone else. Most of us are more likely to be of a danger to ourselves than to any one else. Even the benefits system that we need to survive is made unduly arduous to access and we are always thought guilty first unless proved right.

You might think, what does this have to do with my recovery? Well lots! Take the effect of being on benefits; personally I hate it, I would much rather work but I can't. I need to access benefits to live. The pressure that society has put on people like myself to make me work has made me ill more than once. I came off benefits, built up voluntary work slowly and then I tried to do paid work but I quickly ended up back in hospital. Most of the people who use the system do so because they have to, not because they want to be a drain on society or abuse the system in any way. These suspicions and pressures make me feel devalued and deflated, leaving me with low morale and low self-esteem, and increasing the likelihood of relapse.

# Moving onward and upward

I am not going to go on about the other effects that discrimination can have. You are probably aware of, or can imagine what it can feel like to be marginalised and put on the edge. I needed to point out what effect this can have on an individual who is already struggling to cope with life. I am trying very hard to move forward from the position I seem to be stuck in. The diagnostic label I have also has a hold on me and, while I am trying to view myself as valuable and worthwhile, it can pull me back. I overcome this, to a certain extent, by recognising that doing a bit of voluntary work when I am able means I am giving back to society what I can, and that I can do no more than my best.

In addition to my involvement with the *Psychosis Revisited* training, my voluntary work provides opportunities to teach students and mental health staff by giving them the benefits of my real life experiences in using the mental health system and inspiring them to see past the label and recognise the individual. Hopefully, this will eventually lead to real service improvements. I was motivated to do this because I had had some particularly bad experiences using the services and

I wanted to do something about this for the future. As well as my small amount of teaching, I am now undertaking a part-time distance learning degree. This is something I have wanted to do for a long time and which I can do, with support, when at home and unable to go out. This means I can develop my skills and challenge myself but it is also something I can control, as I often need to take time out and can only work in very small bursts.

Whilst I would not wish my difficult experiences upon anyone else, there have been some benefits. I have gained a unique awareness about myself and the experiences of other people who have gone through similar rough times. I am more empathic and aware of my emotions. I have changed the direction my life was taking. Although I have come full circle back to teaching again, I have had a life experience that no one can take from me, which informs and empowers me at the same time.

Making new friends who accept me for who I am is invaluable and I do believe they are something that I would not have gained without the experiences I have had. I have a new drive and am now motivated to work with mental health services to improve them. Most of all, I have grown as a person to a level of awareness that some people will never attain. Deep depression is awful and I cannot describe how lonely that pit of despair is every time I go through it, but coming out of that depression is like being awake for the first time. Everything is colourful again and sounds are brighter. I live for that time. The hallucinations also have their good points even in the darker times, as some of the experiences are insightful and on some occasions are beautiful.

I don't know what my future holds but I do know that I will continue on this journey of discovery for the whole of my life. This doesn't mean I don't have my bad days or that I won't hear voices, because I do, but I accept them now as a part of who I am. I know that I will get through the bad days and that there is light when things seem dark, and because of this I get through it. The voices can be distressing but also enlightening. In a way, I have rediscovered that natural part of me that just saw the voices as normal in my life and the coping strategies I had as a child I have relearned and embraced. The main thing I have learned through all of this, though, is to be myself. If I am having a bad day and need to cry or sleep, I do, and if I am feeling unhappy I voice it rather than hide it.

I have spent a lifetime hiding my feelings from myself and other people, and doing this made me worse. I have spent my whole life trying to be what other people wanted me to be or what I thought they wanted me to be. It doesn't matter what people think about me anymore. Yes, I would like everyone to like me and yes, occasionally being excluded because of my label hurts me but I just tell myself that I can't help what people think of me. I am me and nothing is going to change that and I wouldn't want to be anyone else. I may have my problems, I may still do and say the wrong things at times but we all do at some point; I am still happy with me. How many of us can say that? I can't change how other people think or act but I can help what I think and do.

It has helped others when they have heard the story of my journey and hopefully when you read this it will also help you to understand just one life lived with mental health difficulties. I hope that you can now comprehend the difficulties faced and that it can also inspire and give hope to you that people can live full lives even within the shadow of the difficulties they face. Recovery is possible, but it will be the individual who defines it. There is no one definition, there never can be, but there is light at the end of the tunnel even though someone might not be able to see it at the time.

# Summary

I initially thought recovery meant getting rid of all my mental health symptoms and difficulties and that I would eventually go back to living a life that was free of all distress. I was led to believe this by my psychiatrist who told me to take this medication and with time, once we get the balance right things will correct themselves. Well, it's been 12 years plus and I would have been still waiting if it had not been for my peer support group and my involvement in my voluntary work, and my own research. How wrong that psychiatrist was to pretend he had a magic wand and how trapped I was for so many years under a cloud of drugs and misguided belief. I just wish on that first visit to the GP that he had taken the time and really listened to me when I said I needed someone to talk with to work through those distressing times, and that I didn't want the drugs he was prescribing me. If he had listened, I believe things would have been very different now. Don't get me wrong, some medication does help and I am not completely against using some, as I still do, but it has to be in conjunction with having someone to work with in order for you to accept the past, look to the future and make changes in your life. I have now defined my own recovery through working with people, psychologists and my peers, in order for me to regain the hope and aspirations I always had buried deep down, that I thought would never resurface again.

## Some thoughts on good practice

It is well worth thinking outside the box and also exploring what is available outside of the services. Peer support and doing voluntary work have been the two main elements that have helped me.

- **Peer support** – I have gained a lot from peer support either from individual peers that I have worked with, met on the acute ward or from group support. This has been essential in my recovery process. I have learnt new coping strategies, built up confidence in a group, made friends, and been able to open up, be myself and help others.

- **Voluntary work** – I may not currently be able to do paid work on a full-time basis but through doing voluntary work I have built up my skills and confidence, felt valued, met inspirational people and given meaning to my life (opening up new avenues) whilst at the same time being able to vary the workload according to my health.

- **The process of discovery** – I have gone through and my continuing journey has been a huge learning curve. It has been at times a frightening and nerve wracking process as well. Mental health workers have helped me through those more difficult times by listening, believing in me, taking risks and by supporting my decisions (even though at times the possible outcomes of those decisions are uncertain). There have been workers who have not supported the decisions I have made on numerous occasions and actively tried to dissuade me. Thankfully, I have always had a stubborn streak because if I had followed their advice I would have failed at the first hurdle. It is my life and I should make the decisions about how I use it, just like anyone else, and yes a part of that is making mistakes of my own but that is the best way to learn. I could not have progressed as far as I have done without taking my own risks and looking back. Even I have been surprised at what I can do now. Regaining control over my own life has been the main reason I have progressed so quickly forward and moved from being that revolving door patient to becoming more independent and having a life I now want to live.

- If I have any advice to give to anyone working with someone who has mental health difficulties, it is to encourage them, and **to offer step-by-step support in making their own decisions**. This might start off by someone making small decisions (which can seem huge at the time) but gradually at the individual's pace this will increase.

- **I now run my own review**, inviting who I want to be there, **setting the agenda** I want to cover and using the expertise in the room to help me to make my own decisions about what support I want and need. I have an **advance directive** covering the support I would like at times of crisis. None of this would be possible without the support of the mental health workers working with me to achieve my goals.

- **Change is possible** – I learnt a long time ago that anybody can change and that there is always hope, even though at times you might not always see the light at the end of the tunnel.

I had forgotten what I had learnt when training to be a primary school teacher and that is if you always believe and treat a child as if they were naughty then they will always behave that way, but if you focus on the good within them and their strengths, they will respond in a positive way. There have been only two workers over the last 15 years that believed in me, even when I didn't, but it was them that made the difference and I started to believe in myself too.

## Chapter 3

# How I gained and continue to maintain my well-being – the fear is often worse than the reality

Anne Beales

In this chapter, Anne Beales, Director of Service User Involvement at Together, explores how her personal experiences, which include living with mental distress, have impacted on her life in general. She uses her knowledge and expertise to draw out some helpful lessons that she has learned in life.

## Nakedness takes many forms

So, here I am in my flat by the sea listening to the worst storm of the year blowing a gale outside. My kitchen is in the middle of a re-fit, courtesy of the MFI sale, and I've just taken my car to get a new wing mirror fitted at a cost of £200, courtesy of the kids who ripped it off for fun. I've had a great weekend though, as now I'm a member of a fancy gym. I have spent time with friends who I truly love (and I think it's mutual) doing the usual eating, drinking and boogying type stuff. I've also had a couple of emails and texts from friends and people I know abroad, as far away as Singapore and New Zealand. I have become a member of the local foundation mental health trust, too.

My family are pulling together, even though we are all so bereft after my lovely uncle Stewart's death and none of them have been blown away in the gusts of 80 mph (yet). I'm just checking my flight bookings for a holiday later in the year while seeing if all the EasyJet flights are cancelled to Scotland today as I'm due to speak at a conference there tomorrow. What a life! But it hasn't always been like this.

At work, I have to check emails constantly, write reports, manage staff, conduct campaigns around service user involvement, fight for funding, manage budgets, overcome barriers and resistance, attend what seems like endless meetings paying heed to details even at a strategic level, and constantly duck criticism or take it on the chin. Nevertheless, I really enjoy the solidarity and laughs with my peers and colleagues, and I feel great at the end of successful struggles, which makes it all worth it. What a job! But it hasn't always been like this.

No, once upon a time, a long time ago, I was in a room alone, listening to the worst storm of the year blowing a gale outside. Filling bowls and saucepans and other receptacles to the absolute brim with water, gave me the sole purpose of my days. This was my strategy for recognising what was a dream, what was a thought and what was reality. I carefully placed paper towels under this vast assortment of bowls and pans, which were laid out in such a way that there was no way I could leave my flat and go out into the world without knocking into one of them and spilling some water. This was my way of checking whether I had actually been out or not – a strange sort of reality check, if you like.

My thoughts were past breaking point and so full always of terrible, humiliating, terrifying scenarios. I imagined myself walking naked in the street and being the only person not to know while all around me people laughed and I had no idea why. I once actually watched my 'personality' (which was like my reflection) leave me at Leytonstone underground station. I waited for hours being too scared to leave, as I had no idea how it would find me again. I thought it wasn't much of a personality but it was the only one I'd grown, so I waited. Eventually I was thrown out of the station, as I'd been standing so very, very still on the platform for what must have been hours. It never did come back, and I wondered later if it had really gone. Instinctively, I knew better than to ask anyone.

Around that time, I asked my mum, dad and brother why I had to go to hospital before I'd finished my conversation with Jesus. Jesus was sitting in a tree. True, he didn't say much, but it felt like a warm and meaningful conversation, which was handy as I was really naked this time (theme of mine, I guess). I was kneeling in the street, where my mum and dad lived. Was this drug-induced psychosis? That's what I was told afterwards. Perhaps it was, but giving it a name like that didn't really matter to me or help me in any way at the time. The pain of the depression, the isolation, the struggle to think clearly in a straightforward way had made me tired to my soul, my very soul, so I wanted to die. Not really end my life; just leave it.

Neighbours saw what was going on – it was difficult for me and my family, at the time and also in the future. Many years later I was speaking at a conference and got a bit of a shock as one of these neighbours – Arthur, who was in the police force – was there in the front row. I learned from this experience to try to check the audience before I speak. Now, I always try to be safe, but expect surprises and often get a friend to go with me in situations that are unfamiliar.

Lessons learned:

- Be very wary of asking people questions about really strange stuff, especially people who have never done strange stuff themselves
- Be very wary of asking anyone who hasn't been through strange and intense experiences, what to do. They often have really weird ideas that don't necessarily help
- Ask people who know – and so won't be surprised by the question, as long as they are in a 'good' space themselves at the time. Some practical suggestions are always worth considering, as even if they don't give you the results you're looking for, you don't feel so helpless, as at least you're trying to take charge of things

# Try and find your hope, as it is true that in life anything is possible

Leaving the life of straight-balanced thinking is not all doom and gloom. Of course, I think it's important to mention the fear, isolation, confusion and despair but I don't want to overlook that intense experiences can change you in a positive way. I had way too much energy and was an angry person. I got politically active via my union and channelled this energy. It was a revelation that I could be positive and stand alongside people from all over the world to fight for what I believed was justice and human rights, to fight for a destiny that was about equality. More about why later!

I ended up working with children who were described as having learning disabilities and I learnt that their often unclouded view of people and situations got to the heart of situations or individuals without any bother. Through being active politically and working with people who used learning disability services, I found a way of living that held meaning and was worth hanging on for, even if at times I only went for short periods before wondering if dying was an easy way of facing the struggles that went on relentlessly in my mind. It was also a time that I recognised how life was so important to some people as I watched them hanging on so tight to it.

About this time, I also discovered that if I drove recklessly, people who loved life would scream very loudly – sadly, it just made me laugh. However, at last, I had found a way of turning my extreme behaviour into a positive. I received praise for the good work I undertook with vulnerable children. I had people listen to my views and began to get used to meetings! Anyone involved within the service user movement will know how valuable it is to get used to such things.

Lessons learned:

- You can have your probation period commuted via the courts to community service – but only if you have a good probation officer
- Bad experiences in childhood, or even in infancy, can make you a strong advocate for others
- You don't have to save yourself first in life and figure everything out in the short term, as long as your journey stops doing harm to others. In fact, using your time to support others is a brilliant distraction from your own agony. It can even bring rewards such as your status within the community (although very badly paid!)

Of course, this was a time when I learned that organisations that existed for the purpose of delivering 'care in the community' misunderstood fundamental issues, such as who holds what responsibility for providing support to individuals to live a valued lifestyle of their choice. There was also a tendency to misunderstand where power truly lies. It was a time where I tried desperately to 'fit in', yet I stood outside with others who were deemed to be on the fringes of the community and who were labelled as 'special'.

I became a qualified social worker, because I believed I could make a positive difference to other people's lives. But, I also began a restless search for a place where the pain and thoughts would leave me alone, somewhere (if I wasn't to die) I could gain peace. On occasions, others would notice my behaviour and ask questions, so I would move on as I was still searching for my own solutions. I moved home 29 times by the age of 32. Yet, I believe I touched many people's lives positively, as I had genuine respect for those who struggled politically for a fairer society. I had genuine respect for the talents and dignity of the people with whom I worked, facing their struggles weighed down with the label of being 'special'.

This was all very much part of my recovery process and I remain convinced that I gained more than those I was supposed to be 'serving'.

## Dark days of isolation and fear

As a little girl, a thought not based on experience or from what I learned, would seem to just pop into my head. Thoughts seemed to be put into my head from the outside and these thoughts were totally unrelated to my life or me. In they would come and there they would stay. On occasions, this meant I could make people laugh as I saw life differently. Sometimes, it meant I provided the energy within social settings and parties, always dancing and playing pranks. The activities and laughter were often proportionate to the isolation and desperation I felt. I was never tired – just on and on the spiral would go, either dramatically up or down. I had no real control of where the thoughts would lead me. I still have powerful memories of being scared when going out in the evenings, as I wondered where I would end up (and with whom). At times, I felt I had to be alone and quiet and still, hoping I would not be noticed by the thoughts and somehow escape them. I saw myself as different to other people.

At school, I have memories of being excluded, which was very difficult for my family, as my adoptive mother was a teacher. I would then exclude myself at school by talking for hours and hours to myself (I liked to believe I was in conversation with Peter Tork from the Monkeys or Terry Wogan). I usually did this in the loo or the playground depending on weather conditions (I was mad, not stupid!) I was put into a 'low' stream at senior school, so I guess, I could have more staff attention. Some of my classmates couldn't read or write and, at break time, the bullies saw my classmates as easy targets. This was not the case for long as they were my classmates now, so I beat up the bullies and we got left alone. Then, although I was always told I was thick at school, I was put into a higher stream and eventually studied to do A levels. I never took the exams, but that's another story! However, I learned plenty at school: I first understood about equality and discrimination there and that I wouldn't tolerate it; I saw no difference between people who had learning disabilities and myself. When the bullies tried to beat up any of the 'minority' young women, from the South Asian community or whoever was seen as different in any way, I was called upon and eventually expected to stand up and sort it out. Perhaps even then the seeds were being sown that led to my working with others to set up service user-led groups.

Lessons learned:

- When you don't know who you are, you have to have a big wardrobe and give yourself plenty of time to choose what to wear!
- Fighting people bigger than you hurts, but their fall is further
- Equality, which is brought about by valuing the fantastic differences in people that makes us all so unique, is our human right
- Being judged can screw you up. People 'in charge' like to judge, as it helps them feel a distance from you and that in turn helps them feel safe

## What was offered to support me, what I ran from, what I expected and what really worked

Once, in my early 30s, I was trying to come off medication following another breakdown. My friends took me on a holiday to Sri Lanka. I rested, laid in the shade, swam and listened to my music (walkman – that dates me!). The food was local, vegetarian and spicy – so gorgeous. I saw wonders, like a statue of Buddha carved into rock in 2000 BC; I saw wildlife, like monkeys and elephants. I came off the medication in Sri Lanka and felt much better. I laughed and talked (slowly at first). The thoughts that plagued me, especially at night, melted into the ocean and every wave took them further out to sea.

When I'm losing the plot, I often phone friends to check out the thoughts I have. I ask if I smell a particular way; I ask how I look, and if there is anything I need to know; I ask if I'm a good person and if I will have to see a doctor. My friends answer and I trust what they say. My friends spoil me with their devoted listening and their indulgence in answering all my questions repeatedly and then I get better. My friends, good food (if money allows for it, then a holiday with sunshine), learning about other cultures, feeling accepted, dancing, swimming, resting and sleep all make me better. Oh, and sex, of course!

I have been told so many negative things by psychiatrists about who I am and where I'm heading. I have taken medication that has made me worse (the smell thing comes from one drug therapy in particular). However, I have had GPs that explain things to me and phone me at home when they are concerned. The funniest was one GP who was – how shall I say – eccentric. He thought I was losing my ability to think straight when I told him I'd gone for a director's post in a national mental health charity, where I'd be organising and supporting the people who accessed the services of that charity. He was asked for a medical report and looked so pained and torn as he explained with genuine concern that he couldn't lie about my 'history'. *'Oh, that's all right'*, I said, *'It's because of my history I'm suitable for the post'*. He wanted to book me for a follow-up appointment, obviously thinking I was 'losing my balance'.

That was more than three years ago and I'm still in the job! Knowing how people who access services can:

- Problem solve
- Offer compassion
- Give sound advice
- Have the courage to speak up and out
- Keep being there for one another
- Learn so quickly from their experiences to support a way forward for others
- Organise
- Laugh
- Try new experiences
- Remain open and hopeful
- Live up to so many challenges
- Stay true to their values and beliefs
- Achieve so much with so few resources

This makes my job within the service user movement the best in the world. Having first learned from all the members at a local service user-led group, I had the privilege to work for a project in West Sussex called Capital (clients and professionals in training and learning). I was asked by members to take the Capital way of empowering people nationally and internationally as that was their aspirations and ambition! So I did as I was told, and I now sit on the management committee for the National Survivor User Network, and I have played a role in establishing Interrelate as an international service user-led network. I can't let some people down and I still wonder what the balance is between what I get out of my work for myself and what I give back. Still, since starting this work, I've felt more balanced, included, and as if I'm living a valued life. I even got an MBE in 2007, although I see this as recognition for the work of many, even if awarded to an individual. The look of pride on the faces of my family – my mum and dad, brother, nephews, aunties and uncle – was worth all the agonising and mind-searching over the dilemma of whether to accept or not. Of course, the criticism rolls in and can get personal. Perhaps, I sometimes try to organise too hastily and have grand ambitions for the service user movement but there are worse ways to live. Life hasn't always been like this!

In my late 30s, I spent five years in psychotherapy, which was provided on the NHS and for two years I went three times a week – it saved my life. I arrived after a breakdown, believing I was dead and was placed on heavy medication. I left knowing I was alive and determined to stay off the medication and to give up smoking (it took nearly another decade but I haven't smoked for over a year now) – evidence that I want to stay around. When I started psychotherapy, I had no relationships that were equal. I finished and now meet the eye of all whom I meet. I've had cognitive behaviour therapy (CBT) too. I see psychotherapy as surgery and CBT as first aid. You need both if you have cancerous thoughts that need removing.

Lessons learned:

- Always listen to those whom you respect and keep them close
- It is people's motives you have to understand when you're being attacked and the going gets tough
- Being involved in the service user movement is a great joy as it supports people to stay 'in control of their balance as individuals in groups', and gives hope to those currently using mental health services and to those who will come after us
- It's tough and hard work being labelled a leader. It means you have to get up earlier and stay up later than most people. It's very useful to have too much energy – well, sometimes
- People who use services have never, not once, let me down

## On balance, then, how have my experiences impacted on my life?

For years I believed I was worth very little and that would have been on a good day. Most of that was both introduced and reinforced by 'professionals' who came into, interrupted and then left my life. In the main, they genuinely wanted to 'help'. They were sincere and highly trained. However, they didn't know me, so it's hardly surprising their intervention didn't work for me and I wonder what they took away from our meetings/sessions. Did they feel my struggle to find peace, a home to live in and a wage earned honestly in the way I did? How did they comprehend equality? They couldn't know the fights against the bullies I had as a child. They couldn't comprehend that the minute they judged (assessed) me I would recoil and feel degraded and misunderstood. They were simply within a system that prevents real partnership and still has little or no understanding about local communities. Even if their buildings are in the heart of communities, they remain outside of them. They didn't inhabit my world, and I (without realising it for a long time) didn't agree with their world and its values. Yes, individuals I met were kind, knowledgeable and skilled but not part of my community and so were lost to me, and I to them. They were not my friends, my neighbours, my companions or colleagues (or comrades!).

So I found my own way, as so very many others have. I hope my community aspirations will inspire professionals to see what is possible when we have the resources to do it for ourselves, so they will support us. Not being a fool, I know that without that support, we have very little chance of success. All of this is not just about ideas. I have been able in the last decade to live my life based on making partnerships work. My work is about raising awareness of the service user capacity, which is just lying in wait to be woken up; the awareness that, once awakened, its capacity can initiate the changes in our lives that bring balance.

I will always need friends, breaks to be alone with myself, time to laugh and money to live where I want to and in the way I want. Then I can deal with the thoughts that harass and try and damage me. After years of rehearsing and practising, I can deal with them quickly and effectively. Only when we all have such opportunities, will we know what is possible. Imagine, just imagine, communities where well-being is a number one priority; neighbourhoods where discrimination is not tolerated, where good-quality housing, employment and childcare are accessible to all, where language barriers are overcome through understanding.

The illness model costs the state and has cost me so much. By not getting it right in the first place, the cost can and does become too high on so many levels. The barriers and resistance to service users' expertise leading change are high, but these barriers will not stop us and resistance will be overcome as we have nowhere else to go. I have listened to people from every continent of the world who have experienced distress, confusion, isolation and fear. They all speak the same language, share the same ambitions and organise in a similar way. This isn't because we have worked together or even spoken to each other. It's the experiences themselves that unite us and compel us towards the same conclusions.

I have had great highs and lows; I have had great loves and friendships, as well as loneliness; I have been on the run and I have stood firm. My life has been a mixture of great successes and horrendous failures. I have travelled and made my home in various places. I've been young and am now middle-aged. I've had insight and I've also been ignorant. I've tried and lived and laughed. At the end of the day, 'mad or not', we are all the same human beings when it comes to life.

And life hasn't always been like this for us. For all of us, everything changes, thank goodness.

Lessons learned:

- Don't tell someone on the first date that you're mad
- Once you believe life can be better for yourself and others, make changes
- Never say 'No I can't'

- Things you learn by being streetwise are good lessons
- Being naïve is not a crime

A final word: in my life I have learned to treat the 'incidental' as just that, focusing on what is important. People and things unseen are important. I'm pleased life has taught me so well.

## Some thoughts on good practice

- As I have received the most sensitive and robust support from service user-led groups, support which has had the most positive impact on my well-being, I believe my self-directed support would take me again and again back to service user-led groups to find my 'balance'.
- I find a warm welcome, acceptance and understanding in such forums. The forum's activities give my days purpose and I found my confidence and value in my skills and knowledge again.
- Practitioners should work in partnership with people, genuine partnership where 'self-governance' is dominant. Staff should know and support local service user-led groups and indeed learn from such forums as they have so much to teach.
- The very step of 'getting involved' to make positive changes to the 'system' we got caught up in, is empowering and therefore improves people's well-being.
- Frontline workers would benefit from having knowledge of and relationships with local service user-led groups.

## Further suggested reading:

Stickley T & Basset T (2008) *Learning about Mental Health Practice*. Chichester: Wiley.

# Chapter 4

# Thank God for the trees!

Big Roy

In this story, I am going to talk about what recovery means for me. When people say there is no God, they want to suffer mental illness – either you'll want God or you'll find one. If people experienced what I feel, they would hope there is a God to save them. Communing with nature – when you sit alone – no matter how bad you feel you can see a meaning to it all (but don't ask me what it is!). What I see as God is not someone sitting on a cloud with a big stick – it is all that is out there – nature.

## Growing up

Life began in an old cottage in a small hamlet. We had one tap and an old range; a copper; some oil stoves and lamps and a bucket loo. I always remember the rats nest over the loo. My Dad spent a lot of his time making traps to get rid of them. The cat hid under the range asleep and did not mind the rats. Across the road we had a piece of land where my brother and I had a garden shed and my father grew food for us all. One memory I have is of an old sort of uncle passing by in a horse and cart and telling us to look out as he threw a rabbit and large swede over the hedge, and we ran indoors for our mother. She made us a lovely lunch. Summer was spent in the fields picking blackberries and gleaning for ears of corn to feed the chickens. Dad always had hutches full of rabbits so a lot of time was spent collecting food. He would push my brother and I around in country lanes in an old cart he had made. We also spent a lot of time kite flying.

All this was about to change as I had to go away to have an operation. It was a long way from home and my family could only visit once a week in a borrowed car. I remember my ninth birthday, it was in hospital and we had deep snow. I felt very emotionally upset thinking my mum, dad and brother would not be able to visit me. They did come with a tiny wind-up toy and a large box of my favourite fairy cakes covered in icing and topped with big cherries. I think I became ill because of the stays in hospital (there were three) and all the experiences of being held down, put to sleep and sometimes coming round with my hands tied to the top of the bed in an empty room and a tube in me, that you did not expect. It was all the more than terrifying – almost unbearable. This hospital had a great effect on my life, from what I saw other children had to suffer from deformities and burns; it can give you empathy for other sufferers. Tears run from my eyes as I write this (can you believe that some call me Big Roy?).

Across the road, at our small cottage, next to our plot of land lay a copse. There I spent many hours sitting under a large tree. In the spring, primroses and snowdrops grew. Birds sang and dairy cows munched the grass in the next field. Around the tree, the ground was covered in short grass and moss – a wonderful way to recover from all the nightmares of hospital. A few years later, I had a job on a market garden and even then there were times when I spent all day picking strawberries with skylarks singing overhead.

School days were some of the unhappiest days. I cannot write here what it was about but there were bullies and when this happens you cannot let them know your unhappy emotions. You have to be brave and carry on with life. It was a relief when school days were over but it brought home to me how tough life can be. I suppose some see me as a clown but I am told they can be some of the unhappiest as well. When these emotions catch up with you at times in your life, you have to cope or go under. Humour can be a good distraction – I think one plus to have come out of being bullied in the shower at school was that it certainly taught me to think of a quick answer.

I did not realise at first, but by the time I was 19 years old I started to develop delusions and for the rest of my life there would be periods of having terrifying nightmares. Now I can rationalise the thoughts to some extent and say that none of this has ever come true, but the feeling is so real that it will happen. You can't describe the limits you are at and nobody else understands. The worst part is the emotional feelings – some you don't know what they are, so that for a great part of my life I have sat under a tree and tried to work it all out.

## Letter written one night at my wit's end

I feel differently now but I want to include the letter below to show how desperate it can feel without any sense of real help out there.

Dear …

*Sometimes in the middle of the night when all is going wrong, I wonder where the help is. You have only two choices. One is to deal with the many problems you have, or to blow your xxxxxxx brains out. This may seem a bit drastic but at that time of night with no one to turn to, that is how you feel. Some may say, phone the Samaritans, but nine times out of 10 they will say they are only there to listen. I had one of them on the Isle of Wight say I was wasting his time and the engaged tone more than once (but this does not happen?). I could sit at home and talk to the wall – this might really bring some help. There is the Mental Health Line but they are not always there (staff problems I am told). And if they are there, there is the feeling they are trying to get you off the line – after all you are only allowed 20 minutes. I have been told by a mental health worker that other patients feel pressured to get off the line. A few weeks ago, I spent a few days in a psychiatric hospital. On release, I was told I could phone the ward office if I needed it. But they didn't remember me when I phoned and the ward nurse is trying to talk to someone else as well. You can hear doors banging and there is some sort of crisis going on. All she can do is take the name of my CPN and let him know in the morning. But she never does.*

*I feel I have no family. Some say why don't I call on them for help but they are not there. Lots of friends support me but how would they feel to be phoned in the middle of the night? Many lead busy lives and need their sleep. If only the dear old support worker would give me her number, I could call her. But would she still love me the next time she visited? There is the other choice – the shotgun. But I have a mental health problem and would probably not get a license.*

*I understand the busy lives people live and the shortage of money for services and all the other problems there are. And, of course, there could be a phone out of order down the line somewhere. Sadly, a dear friend of mine took her life not long ago because she could not find help. Does anyone know where the help is? PLEASE LET ME KNOW. I feel you have to be standing on a chair with a rope around your neck before anyone will really help you. Once, in absolute desperation, I dialed 999 only to be told by the policeman at the other end that I needed help and should phone a hospital!*

*I have been given a wonderful gift – a sense of humour. Let's hope I can turn to this in times of need. Because in the middle of the night there is nothing else.*

*Big Roy*

These are the thoughts I've had in the middle of the night, written at the time. When I wrote this, I really was at a desperate point. I can only compare the emotional suffering with that of a condemned man in his dark cell about to be beheaded in two hours. At this time you are afraid to tell anyone. You will soon search the bottom of your heart in the hope of help. When you have experienced such fear, you will want to enjoy good times to the full.

## Recovery under a tree

In these troubled times, you wonder why this had to be you. Who made you and why did they have to chuck in a few bad bits as well as the good bits? But then look around – even the tree is not perfect – caterpillars are eating its leaves. There is a little grub in the acorn and honey fungus is starting to get at the roots. Yet the tree still enjoys the sun and rain and birds singing in its branches. I expect some of my mates will pull my leg about this, but when you sit under a tree and wonder what the hell is going on, you can find God in the peace and quiet of the tree.

To some extent, I could say that the tree has saved my life several times. Writing down what I see helps – it makes you more aware of your surroundings – you can find different things each time. On some occasions, I have sat in the woods around a camp fire on a November night until 11 o'clock, listening to foxes, badgers, owls and deer. In a bad spell, one day won't cure all the emotional feelings and the conspiracies; but I have seen fox cubs sunbathing; heard a buzzard mew high in the sky; saw a badger carry a hedgehog home for his tea; had hornets fly around by nightlight; seen woodpeckers, tree-creepers and a nuthatch. I have found tawny owl chicks high in the forest canopy and once had a fox that would almost take cheese from my hand. I even had the police give a social call and monks for tea around the campfire.

When I look back to the times of childhood, it seems that I was born in medieval times. Seeing the world today in my mind, it has gone completely mad. What are we doing? We need to look backward not forward. The stresses of the world do not help my mental health. There is no stress sitting under a tree – unless there is a bloke behind you with a chainsaw. I have been lucky to be born with a sense of humour. I think we all need to look at ourselves and see the funny side. Many unhappy things have happened over the years and I am sure afterwards that these happenings are good for the spirit. I think of my schizophrenia as a blessing in disguise because without it I would not have had some of the good times. I have always had a longing to be a monk or a tramp in my life. When I've talked to Buddhist monks about being a clown, they have always said you need to be a tramp and a clown to be a monk. I say you have to be a tramp and a clown to be a schizophrenic.

The times in today's world I have nearly packed a bag and gone – nobody will even know. If I could live in the hedge under a waterproof sheet, I would be happy. Nobody understands why I carry a large bag full of useful bits but if things get too bad it is reassuring to know I could just go. I have sometimes cried and felt the loneliest and the unhappiness anyone could ever get – there is no Big Roy then. When you're really unwell, everyone is either off or the phone doesn't work. I feel frustration about not being able to contact the Samaritans or the Mental Health Helpline. What do you do? The person on the other end isn't you and half the time there is nobody there. All I wanted was someone to talk to and was told by the hospital night staff, 'have a warm drink of milk and go to bed!' When you're really desperate the only thing to do is sit under a tree. I have sat in the middle of nowhere and watched the moon nearly all night and watched the sunrise from the top of a hill and thought what else do I need?

## My ideal support worker

If I could have a wish and have an ideal support worker, I would like someone to be flexible with the time they have to give. Perhaps, when times are tough, they can be with you in the day and arrange other support when they cannot be there. I think this person must understand how afraid you can be at times and how strong your emotional feelings can be. Another thing is how real paranoid thought can be when you are too afraid to tell anyone (even if it were your own mum!). If only someone could sit down and talk to you (with a cup of tea) even if it was in the middle of a field. To gain the confidence of a support worker or another friend is so reassuring, and to know that not all those people in that great big world out there are not in some way conspiring against you.

You do not have to talk to me about the problems that are troubling me at the moment. It could be about the buttercups growing in the field, or the skylark overhead, or some special offer in the supermarket. All this helps me to see that there are some good people and not everyone is planning some trick or other bad deed in the hope you will be put away for life. To me, a conversation with someone about the weather or about a dog with a broken leg does more good than an injection or a tranquilizer. Perhaps in these modern times, the support worker could give out their mobile number so that contact could be made within work time. It would be nice to have cover for weekends as these can be very lonely, but maybe this is some wonderful hope that will never happen. No one knows the lonely life I can live in my paranoid state. The only thing is to enjoy the good times and keep looking for that support worker. **Where are you?**

### Some thoughts on good practice

- Flexibility on time given – to be there for long periods when times are tough.
- Understand how afraid I can feel at times and the strength of this feeling.

- Understand that paranoid thoughts are real for me. Some friendly reassurance helps me to have the confidence to think that not everyone is conspiring against me.
- I don't always need to talk about my problems. Ordinary conversation about the weather or someone's dog with a broken leg does me more good than an injection or a tranquilizer.
- It would help me to have mobile contact with a support worker and some cover for out of hours when I'm feeling bad or very lonely.
- Be flexible on place – it would help me if someone would sit down and have a cup of tea with me, even if it was in the middle of a field.

PS. I think our hospitals are too big and too far away. Too many people have to achieve goals. If more people had time to sit down with you and have a cup of tea it would be better. We need a doctor we know – not one on a flying visit at weekends from 30 miles away. I suppose, like all other organisations, no one has got the time or money anymore. Find a tree.

PPS. Watch nature: when a flycatcher has its nest pulled out by a feral cat and its babies eaten, it does not give up but goes on and builds another nest. A robin sat on my shoulder in the bus shelter and I fed it breadcrumbs and biscuits. It came every morning – wonderful. This was when I was suffering from paranoia. It was almost like a visit from God – enough to reassure you that you are not alone.

One last word – I would like to find that badger that stole my tin of evaporated milk…

What would we do without trees?

## Chapter 5

# The subterranean lift

Mark Edgar

At the time of writing in May 2009, I have lived with my mental illness for 19 years, almost half of my life. Psychosis has been a big part of that illness. Over those 19 years, I have achieved what I believe is a sustainable recovery. The following is a short account of that recovery journey. I have chosen to write a linear narrative as there are specific and notable points in that journey; the date at which sustainable recovery was achieved is identifiable. For many years mental illness defined my life; now it is just a part of that life.

## Untreated madness

As a child at school in the Cambridge of the late 1970s and early 1980s, we'd often talk about being taken away to Fulbourn by the men in white coats who drove a yellow van. It was a child's scare story. Fulbourn certainly existed but we didn't really know where it was. Neither did we have any idea what madness was; it was just a notion that lurked vaguely in our minds. The yellow van took away the 'funny people'. I sometimes mused on why the van was yellow. I never did work out where that detail came from. In fact, in a previous school incarnation, I had already seen one of the old Victorian asylums up close, but that was in connection with suspected, and false, learning disability. However, in the mid 1970s, it was the place that people rarely spoke of and when it was, it was with a certain disdain and trepidation. I didn't associate it with madness – whatever that meant; it was just a place where I'd met a friendly man whom I found interesting and, perhaps more importantly, he found me to be interesting.

I returned to Cambridge in 1988, and by the summer of 1990 that part of my life appeared to be going extremely well. I had spent that year singing, playing rugby, American football, coxing a boat, occasionally working, but above all partying. Life seemed idyllic that June. I wasn't really looking forward to the holidays but I had a car and there were many parties planned, which would take me away from home for much of the time. Some of my tutors felt that I was headed for a first honours in part one of my degree. As I waited for my exam results, there appeared to be few if any clouds anywhere. Under these circumstances, why would I know what psychosis was? Indeed, why on earth would the idea enter my thinking? There were no signs. My world collapsed on 16th June 1990. It was sudden, dramatic, life changing and ultimately life threatening. I had no clue as to what was happening as my life imploded. So started my lengthy battle with psychosis although at that stage, I didn't know what that meant; nor indeed do I think I had even heard the word before. It was a hot and sunny day as I headed, weary, hung-over, and myopic, to collect my post. With me was a girl from Alabama whom I had met the night before at the May ball. She was the unknowing and unwitting witness to my sudden and rapid descent into madness. I found and opened an unexpected letter. As I squinted to read it in the bright morning sunlight, it emerged that the most important relationship of my life had ended; a few words, written on blue writing paper, chosen with care. The change was abrupt.

I was hurled into a world of detachment, uncertainty and confusion. Emotionally I simply shut down from the world. I spoke with lucidity but no meaning. I moved normally but had no purpose. I thought but only of strange things. Maybe that was the day I first heard her voice. In retrospect, the spinning of thought that broke off into voices, thoughts of such speed began immediately. Yet, if someone had asked if I was hearing voices I would not have understood the question. Above all though, was an ever pervading feeling of darkness and despair. How would I get out of this? Would I get out of this? Why? There were many questions but no answers. This was the first phase of my illness, and it would last for the next 13 months. Within days, my results came – a 2:2 – failure in my eyes. Days after that, my cat was run over and killed. Back in Kent, I had a long, lonely, black and despairing summer. Those around me shunned me as a leper, a loathsome and selfish leper, and all the time I only communicated with what was going on in my head. She not only spoke to me, she haunted me. A figure without a face, a light that darted around but never came into focus. I went to all the parties but I was a mere presence; I was not really there.

October brought the relief of returning to Cambridge, but it was a Cambridge I no longer recognised. Before me loomed finals, then what? Nothing – just more blackness. I fought through the year with a deepening sense of impending disaster. I did all the normal things I had done before but nothing brought me joy or peace. From time to time I found myself ruminating on the idea of going to see a doctor, but I always dismissed the idea because I felt they were likely to tell me I was stressed about my finals. Much of the year I felt I was hanging on against something I didn't want to happen. I knew there was a word for it but it was a word I dared not utter either out loud or to myself. That word was suicide. As the summer came I did my exams and suffered on the anniversary of a battle that had started such a long time ago. I got a 2:1 but that made no difference, and Cambridge was over, beyond didn't bear thinking about. The night before graduation I drank myself into oblivion in the Granta pub by the river. Through my drunken haze the answer appeared with an unusual clarity – suicide. I hadn't slept for months. That night I slept well as death neared; there was a way out.

The following day, during my graduation lunch, I had my first panic attack. Two days later, I returned to Kent, alone, scared, and intent on dying. My only conscious thoughts were on how I was going to bring about my own death. The first phase would soon be over. I quickly decided to use the car exhaust in the garage; but I wouldn't be able to get unhindered access until September. Within a month, I had developed chronic, permanent headaches that never shifted. I was still unable to sleep and after that month I finally decided to seek the advice of a doctor in search of some pills. I'd never met this particular doctor before. He seemed quite reluctant to give me pills and wanted to refer me to the local mental health team. He did give me some small yellow pills which he said would help me to sleep. Assuming them to be sleeping pills I took the one prescribed and slept a rare sleep. Sadly, the benefit lasted but one day.

On a blisteringly hot day in late July, I met two members of the mental health team, a bearded man and a Chinese woman. It seemed to take forever. I remember little of the conversation except for two specific questions and a statement. They asked if I heard voices; I answered no as I didn't understand the question. The second question was if I had ever thought of killing myself. The answer was an emphatic, deceitful and evasive no. One of them told me that the pills I was taking were antidepressants and that they thought I had depression. There was some relief at the thought that what I had was recognised, but it was a relief tinged with scepticism. At night I went out alone, either driving or just sitting in the car. Both these were accompanied by endless cigarettes and music. By day I sat in a hidden place by the nearby canal. These were my places; the places I talked to her and thought incessantly about dying; voices and thoughts; thoughts and voices.

During one of my nights in the car in early August, a sudden clarity emerged in my mind. Use the pills. I slipped silently back into the house and in the darkness and peace I downed more than 90 amitriptyline tablets and some painkillers I had left over from an old injury. Slowly I inched my way back up the stairs. I got undressed and neatly folded my clothes on the chair. Then I lay down to die. When I awoke in hospital I could not swallow, had no sense of time, and endured a great feeling of failure. I must try again. Some were kind to me in there. Others, like a doctor who came to visit me one day with a group of adoring medical students, were positively abusive. My sister came and I couldn't understand why she was there; she should have been at work. After some time, although I was unable to ascertain how long, they said I was well enough to go home. Home – what was that? Well, what had changed?

## 'Treatment'

I think it was the following day that the bearded man came to see me. He mentioned his previous question about suicide and looked quite shocked when I told him I hadn't wanted him to stop me. He told me I needed to go into hospital and the next day I was in hospital. I had arrived at the mythical Fulbourn, except this one was in Kent not Cambridge; I didn't know precisely where. It was a terrifying place of metal doors and bars, decay, neglect, despair. There was no care. They simply emerged from the office at certain times of the day, counted heads and then doled out the right number of cups of tea, lunch or dinner. Worst of all, I had no idea when and if I would be allowed out again. How was I supposed to get better in such a place? Then I got lucky. After a few days, a doctor decided that I didn't need to be there and sent me home.

I left scarred, shaken, scared and determined never to go back, but nothing had changed; I was still ill. I had no hope and I wanted to die. Next time I did it I would not fail. Shortly after my discharge I saw the first doctor once again. He told me I was depressed because I didn't have a job. How wrong he was. Maybe I had been right not to see a doctor whilst still in Cambridge. For the next three months I was more or less abandoned. I saw a doctor every few weeks. He changed the pills each time and nothing happened. I was still hearing voices but not really aware what they were; it was still too alien a concept. Things changed in November 1991 when an unexpected phone call elicited an invitation to attend a day hospital locally. I was sceptical but went along anyway; I ended up staying eight years. My stay there did very little to aid my recovery but it did have some important benefits: I had people to talk to; I had something to do; and I could get away from home. It was the people who made the place – remarkable people, and we all shared one thing in common: we lived in our own individual hell. It was there that people started to talk about hearing voices. It began to make sense after a while. My experiences didn't correlate exactly to those of others but it was very similar. Whilst I did not believe I had schizophrenia, I was beginning to doubt whether I had depression either. If I did have depression, why wasn't I responding to medication?

The following spring, still in despair, I finally got to see a consultant. His verdict was much higher doses of amitriptyline and psychotherapy. I began what they told me was called cognitive behavioural therapy. It lasted 18 months and did absolutely nothing for me. Early on I was told by the psychiatrist doing it that I was 'not ill, you just have a lot of problems'. I think I must have missed something there; had she not listened to what I had been saying? The higher doses of amitriptyline did help me sleep but within a year side effects stopped me taking it. I then went on to trimipramine. That did help with the sleep but did nothing to improve my mood. Except for a brief period, I have remained on it to this day. Realising that I was getting nowhere, I sought other treatments. This took me to the Steiner Blackthorn Trust in Barming, near Maidstone. At last, someone listened to me. I did art therapy, which I enjoyed and saw a Dutch counsellor. She was the first to get any grip on my condition. She likened it to being in an underground lift that went up and down below the surface for no apparent reason. The surface was being well but the lift never got there. I described my condition as being stable and unstable rather than well and unwell; I was always unwell. My efforts were frowned upon by the psychiatrists though. I also tried hypnotherapy in my despair; this was rudely and arrogantly dismissed by the people I had come to regard as the enemy.

In the autumn of 1993, the psychotherapy came abruptly to an end and I was told I was being discharged. It had achieved nothing. Life was just as awful as it had been for the last three years. I fell into greater despair. What I didn't realise though was that they too had doubts about my diagnosis. A showdown ensued in the autumn. For the first time I took along an advocate. The previous times I had met the consultant he had barely spoken to me; that changed with a witness there. He conceded that discharge would not happen but stated that he wanted me to visit another psychiatrist nearby and go to London for more psychotherapy as an inpatient. When pressed about diagnosis, he said he was unable to give me one. Subsequent events proved this to be a lie. I visited the other consultant shortly after. We met twice, then he delivered his verdict. I did not have depression, a fact I had suspected for some time, but the verdict was far more damning. I was told I had a narcissistic personality disorder. His explanation made no sense, nor did it appear true. All I had told him was real rather than the delusions he seemed to think I was having. With that a referral was made to London, and after a brief meeting in November, I was put on a waiting list. It would take a while though to recognise just how devastating the effect of such a diagnosis would have on my life.

My arrival in London in March 1994 brought many unexpected things. The four months that I spent there were characterised by polarised moods and emotions, wonderful people, sorrow, pain and great intensity. It was very different from my first hospital spell and I could more or less come and go as I pleased, but that was tempered by the 24-hour pressure. Late in April, my mood slumped precipitously. On a pouring FA Cup final day, head pounding and her voice shouting, I went for a walk along the Thames in the rain. She kept saying over and over again 'I love the rain'. At my absolutely lowest, I stood by the river, drenched and contemplated jumping in. Would I die? Would it hurt? What is drowning like? – thoughts and her voice. Out of nowhere another voice started. It was a man's voice although I didn't recognise it, it was quiet, 'Time to die – time to die'. It grew louder. The two voices started to compete. 'I love the rain – time to die – I love the rain – time to die'.

I don't know what stopped me jumping or how long I was there. At some point I moved slowly back to the ward. I arrived, soaked through. The voices were still there but the battle had subsided. I said nothing when I got back.

I was still quite psychotic when the beginning of the end of London came in June. My ex came to talk to the consultant who, by then, I simply referred to as God. Whilst I wasn't present at their meeting, the impact was immediate. She essentially told him that our relationship was all my delusion. This apparently fitted his ideas and belief that I had a personality disorder and was not ill at all. This was swiftly followed by what was effectively an ultimatum; leave for the ward house and become a day patient or leave and go back to Kent. After some debate, I chose the latter. I left on 29 July 1994. I had made no progress at all. Indeed, now I had a second voice to contend with. The second phase of my illness was over; there would be no more treatment. The final options had been exhausted; I was given a choice and made to feel that I had failed to take the right choice. The fact that, like all the choices I'd been offered, this was a loaded one that did not seem to matter to them; I was untreatable.

# Limbo

Most of the next 12 months was a detached haze for me, but two important things came out of it. I learned what the psychiatrists really thought and I made some friends. The former was both enlightening and scary; the latter brought me the support that would underpin my first recovery. One of the first things I did on my return was to access my notes held by my GP. Contrary to what I had been told, the original consultant had already made up his mind that I had a narcissistic personality disorder and had in fact sent me for a second opinion. The man I called God wrote a particularly damning and unpleasant report in which he concluded I was deluded, had a personality disorder and that the most likely outcome was suicide. But the most interesting part of the myriad of papers was one that referred to 'psychotic depression'. It was the first time I had ever seen or heard any mention of psychosis in my case. A subsequent review of all my psychiatric notes in 2005 revealed something I had missed the first time. The second consultant I saw before London had written that I had been having 'true hallucinations' when I saw him. There was clear evidence that they accepted that I was having psychotic symptoms as early as 1993; accepted, and did nothing. Yet the notes didn't give me any hope, far from it in fact; I just found myself in a state of drift waiting to die.

From Christmas time, small changes appeared in my life. With the help and encouragement of a friend from hospital I started to go out more. I met people in the real world not just the mad world I'd inhabited for the last four years. As the months passed, I got to know more and more people. The following summer was a round of endless parties. Much as these were good, they were but transitory events; I still went to bed at night not wanting to wake up in the morning, and for all the company I was still dangerously detached from reality. At the end of the summer of 1995, my new found friends threw a huge party for my birthday. I was 26 and had been living with my illness for just over five years. As I fell into a drunken sleep that night, I didn't realise that I was about to meet my guide for the next four years; she would lead me out of psychosis and my own private hell. A couple of days later I found myself on the road to Canterbury to meet a woman called Caroline who my parents had discovered. She described herself simply as a 'healer'. I felt like everything else I had tried it was bound to fail, but I was so desperate I would try anything. I spent an hour with her, and for the first time in those five years I actually felt better. The effect only lasted a few brief minutes, but she gave me the one thing above all else that I lacked – hope. I didn't and still do not understand what she does or how it works, but days later whilst visiting an old girlfriend, Caroline's weird teachings sent an aged pet dog wild and I started to believe. Recovery started that day in September.

I visited Caroline throughout the autumn and winter. I could only afford to go once a month but the relief was priceless, but each time I returned to my usual state after a short time. Whilst I was not psychotic all the time, the lift never breeched the surface and I remained ill. My mood continued to fluctuate alarmingly. It was as if I had a psychosis switch in my head that operated without my control; I always went psychotic when my mood was really low. The psychiatrists had more or less given up on me at that point. I attended the day centre but was very limited in what I was allowed to do. I had a new psychiatrist by then but he had no new ideas. He was, however, nicer than my previous one. In addition to Caroline, the other great help in that period was my visits to see my friends in London. That Christmas I went to the ward Christmas party and came face to face with God. Unable to think of anything to say I blurted out that I was thinking of returning to Cambridge to do a PGCE. It was really a self-defence mechanism to prove him wrong but in the coming weeks I mused on the idea. I had a feeling that I wanted to recover the lost year in Cambridge, but there was no way I was well enough. It was however a pipe-dream target.

As the months moved on little changed. I looked forward to a trip to France to sing in the summer, another target. What I didn't know then was that my psychosis was about to get much worse. I survived a gruelling week in France through alcohol and caffeine. My mood was relatively stable whilst I was away. It was not until the very last service that it went wrong. Having made it almost to the end without mishap, the switch flicked. As the organ played the opening bars of Handel's 'Zadok the Priest' high above me in the vaults of Chartres Cathedral, I heard her voice singing. She sang the words in perfect harmony with the organ but it shouldn't have fitted. Filled with fear I wanted to run but had nowhere to go. My mind shut down to all around me; all I could hear was her voice echoing around the vast cathedral. When it was finally over I returned to the place we were staying. I took a shower and felt the walls closing in and the voices screaming. Panic and fear were overwhelming but I still had to maintain my façade. Having eaten in silence, I retired to a bar with the others and drank myself into a detached oblivion. Yet the drink seemed to dissolve the psychosis and as the night progressed, I returned to my usual mask of normality.

On my return to England, I reflected long and hard on what had so far been my most disturbing psychotic experience. It was very rare that I had heard voices outside of my head – I wondered whether to tell the psychiatrist or not. In the end I decided that if I told him he may do something about it. When I spoke with him about the incident he became very interested. He asked me a series of questions and for the first time I felt he believed me and he listened. Despite this interest, the listening, the believing, he did nothing. It would prove to be an opportunity missed. It would take another five years to rectify that mistake. Summer turned to autumn and my life was going nowhere. Yet, again, an unexpected turn was looming. It was in October 1996 that a friend persuaded me to go to a talk about education for people with severe and enduring mental health problems. With great reluctance one evening, I went along and met a man called Ian. Ian would prove to be another vital component to my recovery. He was proposing to start a pilot course at the local college late the following spring to try to get us back into mainstream education. College had been mentioned to me early on by the psychiatrists but at the time had seemed absurd to me, having just graduated from one of the great universities, why on earth would I want to go back to college?

## Another way forward and partial recovery

I returned to part-time education just after Easter 1997. It was very gentle, only a couple of hours late in the afternoon when the college was all but deserted. I learned little initially but I warmed to Ian. He seemed to be a man of conviction, knowledge and belief. He knew that it would be foolish to start early in the morning so planned to schedule things from lunch time to make it easier for us all. More than anything else, it gave me something to do. The pilot ended in June and I decided to sign up for real when it began again in the following September. That summer something else took me by surprise. It was rare that I went out with my parents but one summer's day they asked me if I would like to go out to lunch, unknown to me they had an ulterior motive for this invitation. During lunch my father suddenly announced that they had been checking their finances following his early retirement and they had enough to fly me and him to Jordan on Concorde to see Petra. I was so surprised I nearly fell off my chair. Petra had long been a dream of mine but like so many others it seemed beyond reach. Despite the offer, I was suspicious. What did they want in return? But there were no strings attached and not long after we were booked to go on 1 October 1997.

As my life moved into that autumn, I was 28 years old, and I had lived with my illness for seven years. I still had my periods of psychosis, especially at particular times of the year. Rarely did a day go by when I didn't actively think about suicide. But unknown to me, nearly all the pieces that proved essential to my first recovery were in place. I had so many friends; Caroline's work continued to be effective in limited doses; I was back in education and I was about to go to Jordan, but each time I slipped back it felt as if I had returned back to the bottom again. Jordan, however, proved to be a catalyst for recovery. I went for just under a week and loved it. For the first time I really enjoyed myself for an extended period of time. Not only that, I didn't feel guilty about being happy. I had one day when I briefly became psychotic but it was a fleeting moment. On my return, I was generally happier. Most importantly, Jordan provided the basis of my next step in education. Ian asked me to talk and write about it. I set about researching and writing for the first time since Cambridge. Not only that, I started to write poetry again – at last, a way to express my experiences. I had always feared being judged on what I wrote; now it didn't matter. Progress was happening, it was palpable and I could see and feel it. Even a return to Cambridge seemed more of a hope than before. Maybe, just maybe, I might finally go home.

With the exception of my usual dreadful Christmas period, I continued to make progress through the winter. I had periods of almost highs but these were always tempered by the knowledge that hell was still close by. It was at the end of the winter that the most important breakthrough was made. On my monthly trip to see Caroline, it worked and continued to do so. I felt better. My life now moved along at great speed. That spring, I made two momentous decisions: I decided to start another A Level in the autumn; and I made a commitment to applying for a place on a PGCE course at Cambridge for 1999/2000. Throughout the spring and summer, I set about making Cambridge happen. Knowing that it would be an uphill struggle from the point of view of persuading them I was well enough, I called up all the contacts I had there. I dined in finery, had meetings and refined the application process. With references secured, faxes went to and fro Cambridge to get the wording right. Nothing could be left to chance. I had the feeling that because I could be perceived to be a risk I had to be better at application and interview than anyone else who was out there.

By the end of the summer, everything I could do had been done. I was invited to a dinner in my old college that September to mark 10 years since I had arrived there. Armed with a dinner jacket and my paperwork I travelled to Cambridge. The afternoon before the dinner, I went to the School of Education and handed everything in. Now it was down to others; I had done all I could. I had had my usual ups and downs that summer, but for the most part my mood held out. Sometimes I even buzzed although these periods were always tempered by the knowledge that a return to psychosis could happen at any time. I had found, however, that since my breakthrough that spring, the down times were mainly reactions to bad things going on around me. Even so, I had my usual bad times in June and August.

When the autumn arrived an immediate setback occurred. I had settled on doing philosophy for my A Level. I had toyed with the idea of doing psychology but had been talked out of it by others who thought I might spend too much time arguing with lecturers on the finer points. As term began, it became clear that the college would not be teaching philosophy due to the lack of numbers. Instead, I would have to do it alone in a year through distance learning. I had made a start on some of the set texts during the summer, but I was now delayed by waiting for the package to arrive. When it finally did in October, I was a month behind and much to my annoyance it did not include the works I had read already. It would be harder than I thought. Throughout the autumn term I shut myself away working. It did not come as easily as before. My concentration was not what it had been especially when my mood took a dip. It also required a discipline and determination I had not had to display for many years, but I carried on.

It was during this time that a letter arrived from Cambridge inviting me to an interview for the PGCE in early December. The summer's efforts had paid off and now the ball was back in my court again. I would be going one to one for my future. I could only do my best and hope that I wouldn't be in a low or psychotic state when the time came. Even so, failure would be the unthinkable possibility.

A couple of weeks before my interview date, I found out that my consultant for the last four years was leaving. He would be going just days before I went to Cambridge. Although he had had little to add to anything, I liked him. More importantly though, it became apparent that his move might hold up any medical tests I might have to do should I be offered a place, but that was out of my control. It was a cold wet day as I walked with no coat through Cambridge from a friend's house to the school of education. I was confident about it, though. Arriving like a drowned rat I was set a variety of tasks then called in to be interviewed by two people. That was the day I met Christine. She was a woman I knew by reputation but had never met. She would have a great bearing on my life in the coming years. The interview lasted two hours and we spent most of it talking about my health. When it was over I retired to a nearby pub to watch the rugby varsity match. Having done what I could, I headed back to Kent to await my fate.

It was but a short wait. A couple of weeks later a letter arrived. They offered me a place on condition that I passed any tests from Occupational Health. That, of course, might be a problem.

That said though, my mood immediately went up. I wanted to party, but as the evening drew near it became clear that no one else was about. My mood fell through the floor and the psychosis came back. That was the backdrop to the run up to Christmas. I spent that Christmas at my sister's house, trying to work and fighting my voices. It proved to be the longest period of psychosis for a number of years. Yet I fought on into the New Year's Day. As my mood started to lift I was confronted by the challenge of trying to secure a favourable report from Occupational Health. With a succession of locums in place, this proved well nigh impossible. Each promised to write one, but never did. The months moved on into March and still no report. Then I finally won a five year battle with the DSS for disability living allowance. I had been through two gruelling tribunals and although I had won the second one, they had still refused to pay me. I had involved my MP to no avail and finally had to resort to the threat of legal action. This had done the trick and they paid me some £5,000. The battle had taken its toll on me, regularly causing my condition to worsen and driving me to the point of suicide on several occasions. Now that I finally had the money in my hand, I booked a trip to Amsterdam for a few days and prepared to face my demons alone.

Amsterdam was a roller coaster. I lived every emotion possible for four days. I saw the genius of Van Gogh whose portrayal of madness put my meagre efforts to shame. I ate, drank and watched the world. I had rarely been alone in the last few years as my condition deteriorated rapidly when alone for too long. Now I had to do things on my own. On the final morning after a sleepless night, I walked through the deserted streets. Beyond the central station I sat and watched the water taxis come to and fro. As I sat, her voice came to me. We talked but it was not the tortured conversation of the previous years. She spoke but did not answer me back. There was rare peace by the water. She spoke but it didn't matter. That morning, I finally began to let go of my past.

My return to England saw me focus on two things only: my exams and getting through Occupational Health. Through to spring and early summer I had little luck with the latter; there was still a succession of locums all of whom failed to write the report, but the revision continued apace. I did fear the exams as I knew one would be in the middle of June, the time of year when I was most likely to be ill. True to form, I crashed and sat one exam fighting off my voices and strange, destructive thoughts. By the end of June, though, that part of my life was complete – all I could do was wait for the results. By July I was getting desperate about the report for Cambridge. At my appointment, I met yet another consultant, this one an American. Having made the case, I would not go if he didn't write the report now – he relented. It was then that he really shocked me. When talking of diagnosis he stated that he had read all my notes and felt that he had two choices: to write personality disorder or psychotic depression. This was the first time psychosis had ever been mentioned to me. It seemed they did believe me but had done nothing about it. However, I was left with a more pressing dilemma. If either of those two diagnoses were used, it was highly unlikely I would ever be allowed to work with children. I managed to persuade him to write depression instead and the moment passed. I was unable to challenge the idea of psychosis even though I knew it was true.

Not long after our one and only meeting, I received medical clearance to go to Cambridge. There would be no more barriers to going home. All that was left to do was prepare. Time went quickly that summer. I had certain anxieties about going but these did not dent my feeling of achievement and hopes for the future. My results came in August and I was extremely disappointed not to get the A I wanted, but it had little bearing on my future. September came and on the last night before my departure my many new found friends threw a surprise party for me. It went on long into the night. In the early hours we watched a huge thunderstorm go up the Channel but we remained dry. I wondered if that was a portent of things to come; but it didn't matter. I set off later than I had planned the next day. Now I had something to leave behind; the isolation of my life had gone. Late that September morning I headed home to Cambridge where it had all started. I had been ill for nine years and three months.

Going home to Cambridge was supposed to have been the end of the story. To many around me it appeared as if I had been cured. Part of me, of course, wanted to believe that, but through my nine months in Cambridge doubt still haunted me. Those nine months were extremely hard and I had two major bouts of psychosis. I didn't have any treatment other than what I had already. Making things more complicated was my decision to keep all but a very few in the dark about my secret past. I found out after that many of my peers thought I must have been in prison because I was so vague about my past, but Christine was unstinting in her support, and the following June I completed the course. It was only then that she revealed that all of her colleagues she had consulted over my case had told her not to go anywhere near me. On my return to Kent, I found out that none of the doctors thought I would get through the course, but I did, and on 1 August 2000, I was awarded qualified teacher status. The one thing I lacked was a job to go into in September. Indeed, I had not even been offered a single interview, but during that memorable summer it didn't matter; I was on a great high. Unable to take a teaching job, I accepted an offer in November to work part-time as a learning support assistant with Ian at the college. It would be the nearest I ever got to a teaching job. Days later though, my world collapsed and I was struck by a devastating relapse. I was back where I had started.

Once again I was referred back to the mental health team; they ignored the referral. When I eventually got to see someone it was the same old story. *'You're not ill you just have a lot of problems'*. Change the medication and come back in three months. The new medication had a profound effect on my immune system and I had more physical illness in six months than I had had all my life. I couldn't make my next appointment and they never got back to me on an alternative date. They did nothing for six months. When the side effects got too much for me I went back and saw another psychiatrist. He said I could come off the medication but I would need to speak to his replacement as he was near the end of his placement. He commented that she was 'very experienced'. I had little faith; but it proved to be unfounded doubt.

## A simple solution and sustainable recovery

I first met the woman who changed my life early in the summer of 2001. I was expecting little progress and was rather surprised when she asked me what I thought I had. I talked of psychosis and depression, particularly my firm belief that the former was true. Her comment was to ask if I thought the two were mutually exclusive. This was unheard of in my experience, a psychiatrist who asked the opinions of a patient. She rapidly dismissed any notion that I had a personality disorder; in fact, she was dismissive of the whole concept. To her it seemed blindingly obvious after about 10 minutes that I had a mood disorder and asked if I had ever thought of going on a mood stabiliser; no one had ever offered me one. Thinking she meant lithium we talked on. It was only then that she suggested something completely unexpected: risperidone. She gave me other choices as well and asked me to go away, do any research I wanted and have a think. I came away from the meeting at last feeling that I had found a psychiatrist who not only listened but also had new ideas. We met several times that summer. I'd known immediately that if I was to try anything it would be risperidone; I'd only heard good reports of it although I'd never heard of it used to stabilise mood. At that time it was not licensed for such a purpose.

There was but one thing troubling me about going onto risperidone. Only a year before, during my high the previous summer, I had considered coming off medication altogether. Now I was faced with the prospect of not one but two different medications. By summer's end though, I was so desperate, I agreed to try it for three months. If it didn't work I would come off it; I did not expect it to work. It was early in September when I went home with a week's supply of risperidone and instructions to take 1 mg that evening. She wanted me to return in a week. That evening I took the tiny white pill. Then the miracle happened. Within minutes of taking that single pill I felt better than I had in years. The effect, both miraculous and instantaneous; a single pill changed my life. The subterranean lift described so many years before exploded through the surface, went up and stayed up. I had recovery in a lasting and meaningful way for the first time in 12 years; I had my life back.

I returned the following week with news of the miracle. She checked for side effects; I had none. We talked for a while and she asked me to return in two weeks. As I walked out I didn't realise that it would be the final time I would see her. Her last words to me were 'it will be interesting giving you a specific diagnosis'. The price I paid for that last meeting is that I was never able to quash the ludicrous idea that I had a personality disorder; losing her was one of the great regrets of my life. Labels stick and few in psychiatry ever appear willing to dismiss this dangerous, damaging and over-used term. The advent of risperidone has changed my life beyond all recognition. It has given me back life itself. For years I existed rather than lived; now I live and have a great will to live. This is the very essence of recovery for me. Suicide seems absurd now. Rarely do I hear either of the voices that so plagued and tortured me, in fact, I've not heard her voice in years. Sometimes when I get very tired and stressed I dip fleetingly into the old world of psychosis. Sleep and stress are the biggest relapse indicators so I have to look after myself, but I now have the tools to fight my illness when it occurs.

In the summer of 2006 I had a relapse. I had to take time off work, much to my annoyance, but with my varying of the dose and stepping back from my life I contained the incident within three weeks. I had no intervention other than to ask for a sick note. Prior to risperidone, the episode would have lasted many months. Even then I was able to stave off full-blown psychosis. For so many years I would never have been able to do that. For me, recovery is a fluid state; I am not recovered, more in recovery. My state of mind and mood varies just as anyone's does. Yet in my case, as with anyone with a mood disorder, the variation can be vast and dangerous. At the lower end of the scale is when I fear the psychosis, but it is now largely contained. Since that period, I have kept a track on my mood using a scale that is unique to me. This helps a great deal, allowing me to measure where I'm at on a daily basis and to track what in my life is impacting on my mood. More than ever now my fluctuations are due to external factors. Before, I had no control over the switch in my head that controlled my psychosis. Mostly there was no reason for me to go psychotic, but risperidone has also brought a great deal of reflection on my life. Two questions in particular occasionally occupy my mind: what went wrong in my treatment? and how different would my life have been had I found risperidone earlier?

There were two critical missed opportunities during my psychiatric 'career'. In 1993, when they accepted I was having psychotic symptoms and again in 1996 after my experience in France, when they listened but did nothing. I'm actually quite glad I was not put on antipsychotics in 1993, knowing what was available then, but my life could have improved so much had I been put on risperidone in 1996 when it was available. Of course, what I can never know is how much of my recovery is down to Caroline, Ian, education, friends and the many other things I tried. There is simply no answer to such a question. However, I would suspect that recovery would have come about much quicker had that course of action been taken five years earlier. The most tantalising question is, why did one doctor get it right and all the others miss what was apparently very obvious? I can't specifically answer that question but I would go so far as to suggest that they were looking in the wrong place. I have worked in mental health since 2002 and constantly hear comments on the medical and social models. Whilst many talk of overuse of the former, where they failed with me was to overlook it. They gave up looking for a medical answer because they thought they were dealing with issues of personality and behaviour. In fact, there were clear indications that the problem was medical. None of them ever bothered to find out who I was before I was ill. They failed to talk to anyone from my past except my ex and my parents. Many of my friends could have told a different story. That said, the answers even if they could be found, do not really impact on me; I have my life back. I have met so many extraordinary people on my journey; people I would never have met otherwise. That is a blessing. I was once asked at a training day if I could have my life over again would it be without psychosis, the answer to that is no.

My life has been delayed by illness but not destroyed. I didn't get off benefits until I was 33. I was almost 34 when I finally got a full-time job and lived independently. By the time I was 35, I had written the book I always swore I would, which helped a great deal. The 10-year delay in getting the help I needed is an irritant but I cannot change that. Without the mistakes of others, that may have been sooner. For the most part I bear people no malice. There are a few, though, that I fear I may never forgive. The man I knew as God is not one of them, but two things he said to me will always stay with me. He refused to give me a diagnosis on the grounds that I might think that I'll '*find a better shrink somewhere who can help [me]*'. The second was '*I don't think you'll ever find a medication that will help you*'. He was wrong on both counts – very wrong.

## Reflections

Over the years I have been privileged enough to meet many remarkable people. Most of them have been service users, clients, patients and nutters. I find it interesting that although I feel very much part of a homogenous minority group, no one can agree on a common acceptable term to describe us. The debate seems to go on endlessly and probably always will, but more important than anything is the fact that I am a person, the equal of everyone else. Sadly, I have met fewer remarkable practitioners on mental health. During my time in the system they were few and far between. Having since worked in both statutory services and the voluntary sector I have met a few more. The really great ones share certain traits, which make them so special and successful. Some are mentioned here in this chapter, Caroline, Ian and Christine are but three. Heather who is briefly mentioned as my advocate had and still has a remarkable impact on my life. She has always been a mentor to me. The other Heather in my life, the psychiatrist who saw through the fog and took me for who I am was another. The late Jack Byrne, friend, fitness instructor and professional, so well known in Kent mental health circles, remains a great inspiration to me.

There are two great traits that each of these people share: the ability to look beyond the label, and they gave of themselves. They all have a human face and treat the person, not the perceived problem. With the exception of Dr Heather who sadly left my life very quickly, they all remain my friends today, Jack of course would be too if he was still alive. I try to take all the lessons I have learned into my work today, I give of myself one way or another and try to retain a human face. I try above all else to see the person not the label. One thing that has always baffled me is the way in which boundaries are so rigidly preached, imposed and stuck to. Too often these become a barrier to recovery. Sometimes I tell my story to people I meet. This is generally frowned upon but on the occasions I have done so it has universally had a profound, lasting and positive impact on the lives of those I work with, but I will only do this if it is likely to help them and not me.

There are many things that retain the feeling of them and us, the gulf that often exists between workers and those in receipt of services. That gap needs to be narrowed and I don't believe that it will ever be fully bridged, but a move away from rigid boundaries has to be a positive move. There may be good reason for boundaries in some cases but we must not let these hinder recovery. The worker is there to help and guide but it is the individual who has to undertake the process of travel that is recovery. They must be at the centre of that process. I am no more important than the students I now work with. They have the same rights as me and those have to be respected. I think I'm often a bit of a maverick when it comes to my work, but I always try to seek what will best help an individual. Sometimes I am criticised for my approach but it seems to work well. The proof always lies with those who work with me. It is a privilege for me to work with them rather than the other way round.

Working in mental health is fascinating, it is rarely boring and infinitely variable. Sometimes it is hard but it is nearly always worth it. My work is one of the many factors that sustains my own recovery.

## Some thoughts on good practice
- Don't let boundaries become barriers.
- Be flexible in your approach – service users often communicate in different ways to workers.
- Be prepared to take calculated risks – by not doing this it can reinforce how stuck some service users feel.
- Try to get to where the service user is at rather than expect them to come to you.
- It is not necessarily a bad thing to give of yourself – your experience may be enormously valuable to a service user.
- Do not let power positions get in the way – service users are sometimes frightened and distrustful of people they may regard as the enemy.
- Respect service users – they are your equal in terms of rights.
- Some workers may have experienced mental health difficulties and although it may be risky to share that information, it can be extremely effective in aiding recovery.
- Strive to normalise the experience – we all go to the supermarket, restaurants, pubs etc., so why shouldn't a service user?
- Do not mistake the needs of service users necessarily to be the same as those of their carers – they often differ and may conflict.
- Meet in a place of the service user's choosing – in some cases pubs can be acceptable although this is not always wise if a service user has a problem with alcohol.

- Accept that the relationship with service users is a two way street – you as workers must always strive to learn from your service users.
- Never patronise service users.
- Try not to be too judgemental – there may be service users you find to be challenging but they still deserve respect.
- Don't get too hung up on a label or diagnosis – these can be misleading.
- The last point is quite simple, be polite and friendly – you are not there to be a friend but it should not stop you being friendly. Shaking someone's hand or having a cigarette with them can really help to break the ice. On this last point, I'm sure it's against policy but I've never been a fan of such things!

# Chapter 6

# Pause for thought

Ruth Chandler and Mark Hayward

*The thinking that addresses the undecidable is the thinking of tolerance, the thinking that does not sever, the thinking capable of concavity, of turning in on itself to make room for difference*
(Cixous, 1997).

In the introduction, we talked about how the core assumption of them and us was a powerful obstacle in language and action to peer collaboration between the 'worlds' of people working at the frontline of mental health services, and people that are experiencing or have experienced 'worlds' that are very different from what is considered normal. Helene Cixous' emphasis on the undecidable opens the language of 'not' into a way of thinking that is more hospitable to differences that do not fit the categories we habitually use to make sense of the world. To respect these differences, the editors took a minimalist approach to framing and interpreting the narratives while recognising that no narrative arrives without a context and that this will be shaped by different organisational and personal pressures as well as very different power relationships. If you have made it this far into the collection, it is very likely that you may have noticed that each contributor has interpreted the meaning of 'psychosis' and 'recovery' very differently within the common aim of handing over some practice points that could be helpful to frontline mental workers and people that experience psychosis and which would have been helpful to them at the time. In doing so, each contributor expresses a desire to break down the 'them/us' and join hands with agencies of support to create meaningful recovery pathways.

In this middle section, we want to pause for thought about the diverse worlds that readers bring to the narratives. Like the narratives, every reader brings a unique context to their understanding of mental health, which, in turn, is informed by local contexts, organisational and personal pressures and different power relations. What you take out of the narratives will be informed, in part, by the *habitus* of your local context; that is all the little habits of language and action that structure your social space. How are we to make sense of all these different contexts without reducing them to a stereotypical view of what 'recovery' and 'psychosis' is? Too much diversity at one go can be overwhelming. How are we to make it feel safe to work with people whose unusual experiences trigger the organisational anxieties of risk adverse culture or cultures? Who do we mean when we say we? To address these challenges, we set out two frameworks that support recovery-orientated practice and that are hospitable to differences between people. We propose them as a minimal method for working with the diversity and complexity of lived experience, while taking a sober view of some of the practical obstacles to implementing them.

## Radical collaboration

The emphasis of radical collaboration is on relationship building, on meeting the person rather than the clinical problem. There is room for medication. For the people for whom it works, medication provides a meaningful platform of stability from which effective relationship building can proceed. There has been a tendency in recovery literature to define itself as 'not' medical knowing, setting it up as a point of departure from which recovery-orientated practice starts off on a journey without a destination. The notion of a shared recovery destination for everyone is problematic. However, back door universals are not that helpful in co-constructing a meaningful space where recovery can be considered in dialogue with diagnostic and prescribing expertise.

Symptom reduction is still a valid dimension of recovery, especially if the person in recovery sees this as both desirable and helpful. Nevertheless, the commitment of radical collaboration is to a process, not to a clinical outcome. If a clinical outcome occurs, this may be a welcome by-product but the emphasis is on mutual learning between the expertise of mental health workers and people who experience psychosis. Radical collaboration defines itself within and against CBT. It is a common critique of CBT that lived experience is reduced to cognitive 'distortions' from a model of 'correct thought', which remains unspecified. It is very much the responsibility of the practitioner to explore ways to correct these distortions in an evidenced-based way. In radical collaboration, mental health workers cannot assume responsibility for a person's progress, as this responsibility is shared and learning takes place irrespective of outcome.

Seeing the person before the clinical problem opens up different kinds of working relationships with different kinds of starting assumptions built into them. Working from a humanistic perspective, Chadwick (2006) challenges the way people that experience psychosis are understood through languages of defect, lack and risk. Rather, the core of people that experience psychosis is essentially positive. In adverse conditions, sleep deprivation or trauma, for example, anybody could have a psychotic experience. It therefore follows that in different conditions, anybody experiencing psychosis could potentially move towards emotional well-being. Experiences of psychosis are better understood as part of a mental health spectrum rather than an opposition. There is no clean line between madness and sanity. Delusions are not present or absent 'symptoms'. They are multiple dimensional experiences that are on a spectrum with ordinary experience. The question is one of degree rather than kind. For example, it is 'ordinary' to feel itchy when one sees insects without any physical contact with them. It is less ordinary to vividly experience giant bugs walking up and down your arm without any physical contact with them. Both may be understood as imagined aspects of reality. The insects are not there in either case. The difference resides in the intensity of the impact of the imagined insects on the emotional well-being of the imaginer. [1]

For Chadwick then, psychosis is part of the human condition, moving away from illness as the defining feature. Although it is presented as a therapeutic framework, it is easily converted into ordinary relationships. The responsibility of mental health workers is to create conditions of acceptance in which radical collaboration can occur. *'Warmth, empathy, caring, genuine regard and competence'* are core ingredients of environments that support relationship building (Beck, 1995, as cited in Chadwick 2006). In relationship building, it is not necessary to search for 'causes' of psychosis in order to understand a person's distress. It may be that a person experiencing psychosis finds causal explanations a further source of distress or, alternatively, a source of reassurance. However, for Chadwick, it is enough to understand what is sourcing the distress, for example, stress from work or family relationships, because there is no expectation of the worker to make sense of these understandings in a therapeutic framework; it is supportive of relationship building at the level of everyday interaction.

Meeting the person (rather than a set of problems) involves being a person yourself. By being yourself more fully, you can model interpersonal behaviour and reduce the likelihood of the conditional acceptance that people routinely experience. Chadwick (2006) points to two kinds of listening that support relationship building, associative and active. Associative listening is when a person is waiting for 'an opportunity to say something themselves'. Once a connection is made with their experience, they become 'self-focused and look for an opportunity to speak'. Active listening, alternatively, seeks only to understand the world of the person speaking. Listening is not blocked by thoughts like 'when will there be a gap in this conversation'. While Chadwick argues for active listening as being more supportive of relationship building, both kinds of listening support mental health workers and people who experience psychosis to be more fully themselves in a conversation. Associative listening can be helpful if by making a connection with personal experience bridges the gap between the worlds of the two speakers. It is unhelpful if it persistently overrides the desire to understand the world of the other. Beliefs about being listened to are evidence-based. If people have been routinely ignored, they may expect this from the start and/or be interruptive and self-focused. It is important not to be judgmental about this when it occurs. For people who are linguistically vulnerable, that is people who inhabit worlds that make little sense to most people, an associative leap, or interruptive step into the more mainstream worlds of mental health workers may be the first step into this world.

Reader response follows a similar pattern to active and associative listening. Readers either inhabit the space of a narrative through closing the gap between themselves and the person telling the story, or they read at a distance, looking for ways to frame the narrative from their current understanding. Before moving on to the next section, ask yourself the following:

What kind of reader am I? Am I interested in finding out about the different worlds of people that experience psychosis and/or making a connection with my personal experience? There is no right answer here and it is quite usual to juggle with both tendencies. Which impulse has the upper hand in response to the narratives so far?

You may wish to list the parts that have stood out to help you answer the above.

## Risk and safe uncertainty

In the *Psychosis Revisited* workshops, most participants had little trouble with the ideas of relationship building and seeing mental health as a spectrum. New mental health workers had little problem with being themselves in relationship building. The people that struggled with this concept were workers that had been schooled in the notion that strict professional boundaries were an essential part of their role as a mental health worker. Yet, the person-centred skills that support radical collaboration, the active listening described above, for example, are ones that the same workers would not hesitate to use with people with less stigmatised diagnoses. Time is often a significant obstacle to thinking about effective relationship building. However, when time is available there may be a learned reticence to 'think' as this may highlight uncertainty, 'not knowing' and personal vulnerabilities.

What else is going on with this learned hesitance? Chadwick suggests that beliefs about people who experience psychosis as being dangerous can impact negatively on all components of relationship building. For example, you might think that you need to be *especially skilful and careful to avoid sparking anything*' (2006). Whether you are a mental health worker or a person with either direct or indirect experience of psychosis, it is very likely that you have encountered the language of risk at some stage of your experience. This arrives in many shapes and sizes. You may be working within policy frameworks in which definitions of risk are operational in the kinds of space you can make available to people. You may have been taught or read that people who experience psychosis present a greater risk of violence and/or threat to safety. This myth, perpetuated by media scaremongering, has as much cultural currency within statutory and voluntary sectors, as it does in the public domain. Yet, there is no evidence to suggest that you are at greater risk from a person who experiences psychosis than any other person. In litigation culture, the perception that this is so is usually fuelled by generalisations from a small number of high profile cases where a violent incident has followed a serious lapse in statutory provision.

How is it possible to move past the language of risk and reactive response and still keep people safe? One way is to use risk assessments as an opportunity for relationship building. By having a shared conversation about the different perceptions of risk in the room, it may be possible to jointly arrive at recovery goals, which negotiate these or to engage in positive risk taking. However, the word risk itself already invokes a defensive posture and sense of threat that is not supportive of relationship building. People that experience psychosis have enough paranoia without having it embedded into the procedures that structure their lives as well.

Barry Mason (1993) suggests an accessible framework for workers to position themselves in relation to certainty and uncertainty. Writing over a decade ago, Mason suggests that one of the legacies of Thatcher/Reagan/Bush years has been a *shift towards certainties, getting it right, finding solutions*'. Working from a context in family therapy, Mason suggests a concurrent, opposite shift from first order therapy to second order and observer dependent questions of fit. That is, in a first order perspective *a family would come with a problem, the therapist would discover/diagnose what was wrong and with the use of their skill and expertise, lead them back to health*'. The notion of a 'solution', out there just waiting to be discovered is particularly problematic as it supports the notion of something fixed and final to be discovered. This is a position of 'unsafe certainty' in so far as it is unreceptive to differences that challenge the truth of its model. Mason suggests a shift away from certain knowing and first order therapy to *owning a position of uncertainty which orientates the therapist to explore with a family, ideas and meanings which they bring*' (1993).

Like Chadwick, Mason's therapeutic model is easily converted to ordinary relationships between mental health workers and people who experience psychosis. Mason suggests that people often look for help in two states of mind. A position of unsafe uncertainty is when it is believed that options for change have closed and there are high levels of anxiety about what to do. To move away from this position, the hope may be that *a trained person in mental health can change my situation*' (Mason, 1993). The worker is looked to as the provider of 'safe certainty'. Alternatively, people may arrive too clear about what should be done and thereby limit their options for exploring other possibilities. This is a position of 'unsafe certainty' which, again, looks to the mental health worker to be the provider of safe certainty.

Mason uses the example of government reports into child death from non-accidental injury to draw out the way organisations can operate as if they were in the domain of 'unsafe uncertainty', and look for a position of 'safe certainty' as a corrective to this position. Without in any way trivialising the seriousness of the events or downplaying the importance of safeguarding children, Mason suggests that lengthy checklists for ensuring that the same thing does not happen again led to UK social services in the 1980s acting as if they were in the domain of unsafe uncertainty, aiming for a position of safe certainty through an *'increase in checklists, procedures, guidelines and regulations'* (Mason, 1993). These precautions are indispensable but limited by the belief of safe certainty, which attempts to approach child protection like an exact science. Safe certainty is an illusion. Moreover, if it could be reached, the result would be a static situation in which change could not take place.

Problems arise when workers react to people who experience psychosis as if a position of safe certainty were possible. Mason talks about large numbers of social workers leaving their jobs through despair and depression through not being able to achieve a position where they had 'covered everything' – through having 'failed' to arrive at an impossible position of 'safe certainty'. The construction of 'safe certainty' as a 'solution' for positions of unsafe certainty and/or uncertainty has some bearing on the question of risk and learning about people who experience psychosis. High-profile investigations into serious incidents rightly aim to make sure that lessons are learned and all that can be humanly done to prevent a recurrence is put into place. However, this can also result in adopting a position of 'unsafe uncertainty' towards people that experience psychosis, aiming towards the illusion of 'safe certainty' as a corrective. Taken to extremes, organisational risk management can operate as if 'everybody' might behave like that (and usually at the same time!). The desire for safe certainty leads to a position of unsafe certainty insofar as it is impossible that everybody could do this, closing down openness to new potentials for the majority of people. While 'safe certainty' is impossible, the belief that it is achievable can close down hospitality towards difference.

Mason proposes a start position of **safe uncertainty** to counterbalance the language of risk. Instead of trying to find the 'true' path of 'safe certainty', it is more realistic to acknowledge that it is not possible to cover everything. There is a need for a different kind of enquiry that keeps safety central while acknowledging that *'uncertainty is part of the human condition'*. Solutions, Mason argues, are *'only problems that were less of a dilemma than they were before'*. Curiosity that is respectful rather than intrusive is central to co-constructing a space of safe uncertainty between mental health workers and people that experience psychosis. The *'less curious we are, the more we understand too quickly leading to a position of premature certainty'*. Uncertainty does not mean that expertise is undermined. Rather, **authoritative doubt** involves holding uncertainty and expertise together. That is recognising that it is impossible to account for everything at the same time while keeping safety central within the variables that can be managed.

Collaboration can only occur once a position of authoritative doubt is reached and may take place in unequal power relations. It is important to acknowledge that peer collaboration is an ideal rather than a reality in many mental health settings. If a person is compulsorily detained, the power relations from which collaboration proceeds are not equal. However, without the hope of peer collaboration to aim for, there is little hope for recovery to support the present ground of interaction between people who experience psychosis and frontline mental health workers. Holding this hope can be difficult when all the evidence of experience seems to point in a different direction. Further, moving from the desire for safe certainty to the authoritative doubt of safe uncertainty can be anxiety producing for all parties. Nevertheless, without hope for peer collaboration between different and equal parties, there is no incentive to work towards lessening the power differentials between mental health workers and people that experience psychosis. Restraint in an inpatient setting is a good example of this point. If workers hold the ideal of peer collaboration in mind, they will do everything they can before resorting to this measure and everything they can, if they have to implement, to use minimal force and to work towards a more respectful relation. If the ideal of peer collaboration is not there, then there is little incentive for the worker to use the minimal force necessary or to work with the minimal loss of dignity, opening onto potentially abusive relationships. As with Chadwick, it is important not to be judgmental about safe certainty as an anti-collaborative position. Acute inpatient and forensic care are the hard ends of frontline work. These situations are full of demands for safe certainty as a corrective to the unsafe certainty/uncertainty that people looking for help bring into them. Further, these environments can and do boil over into confrontation between these demands and workers' inability to meet them. The difficulty is when workers respond as if they could supply 'safe certainty' or, even worse, internalise it as a defence from the unsafe certainty/uncertainty that surrounds them. To move beyond this impasse, it is important not to be too negatively critical about desire for safe certainty as an anti-collaborative position. Rather, intolerance of uncertainty needs to be gently and extensively unpacked in an empathic rather than condemnatory manner.

Where would you place yourself in Mason's framework? Is uncertainty a safe or unsafe idea?

## Who do we mean when we say we?

Both Chadwick and Mason lay great emphasis on building relations with and expressing curiosity towards the person at hand. We want to conclude by asking who this person is. From Mason's perspective, there is a potential tension in Chadwick's argument regarding the assumption that there is a core conception of personhood to be actualised in collaboration. The idea that this is so could be regarded as a position of unsafe certainty about what humanity is. Martin Mcguire (2005) argues, alternatively, that the worlds that are made visibly human in a social context renders the reality of other worlds invisible. These worlds have not gone away through becoming invisible. 'Rather, the invisible is what has been mis-placed – and re-placed – allowing for the appearance, the **visibility**, of another kind of world' (Mcguire, 2005). One of the challenges of listening to people who experience psychosis is that they bring meanings and experiences that put definitions about what it means to be a human being into question. Different worlds and potentials for being may become visible, rendering your world temporarily invisible or displaced.

Being rendered invisible in conversation is a regular occurrence for people that experience psychosis, as these worlds may often be far removed from worlds that are culturally shared and it is hard to recognise them. That is, there are contexts that are easy to exchange because most people have heard about them, and contexts that can seem nonsensical because not very many people have heard about them. This can lead to a feeling of professional vulnerability (feelings of not being competent or skilled enough) and increased 'linguistic vulnerability' on behalf of the person who may have already experienced many conversations in which their meaning and context has not been listened to or has been named in wounding or stigmatising ways (Butler, 1997).

From Chadwick's perspective, it is the desire to understand rather than the understanding itself that is most important. Asking a person who experiences psychosis to help you understand their world is not an exposure of ignorance or lack of training. Rather, it is an approach that recognises the limit of its understanding and seeks to find out more. From a perspective of safe uncertainty, there is no way of knowing for sure whether the core of people is essentially positive although it is easier to be optimistic and hopeful if one works in this belief. For a Hindu or a Buddhist, however, the idea of a personal self is an illusion to be sloughed off through mindfulness and meditation techniques. There is no sense of past or future in mindfulness and it is a way of gaining some respite from sources of distress and/or ability to roll with them. Different cultures have different ideas about what the core components of personhood are and some would not recognise the concept at all. In 21st century mental health services, it is perhaps prudent to work on the assumption that radical collaboration that also supports a position of safe uncertainty is a shared multicultural space that cannot be decided in advance by either party.

Before turning to the next section, ask yourself the following:

How do I understand personhood? Do all people have core features in common or are there irreducible differences between them? Is uncertainty about these questions threatening or an opportunity for adventure and new learning?

Everybody stands in a different place in relation to the themes above. Uncertainty can be liberating but it can also be very disconcerting if your local context is saturated by desire for safe certainty. It is worth honestly noting your responses to the questions raised throughout. You may wish to go back over the previous chapters in the light of these or take them with you to the next section. To make best use of these supported discovery frameworks, ask yourself how you would build a relationship with each author if you met them today. How would you express your curiosity? Whichever direction you choose to take, ask yourself how your responses structure your understanding of what 'psychosis' and 'recovery' is. Which aspects are most visible to you? We will return to these themes in the concluding section.

## References

Beck JS (1995) In: P Chadwick (2006) *Person Based Cognitive Therapy for Distressing Psychosis*. Chichester: Wiley.

Butler J (1997) *Excitable Speech: A politics of the performative*. New York: Routledge.

Chadwick P (2006) *Person-Based Cognitive Therapy for Distressing Psychosis*. Chichester: Wiley.

Cixous H (1997) In: M Calle-Gruber *Rootprints: Memory and life writing*. London & New York: Routledge.

Mcguire M (2005) *Visible Humanity: Cultural-historical considerations for postmodern psychology* [online]. Available at: www.RadPsyNet.org (last accessed April 2009).

Mason B (1993) Towards positions of safe uncertainty. *Human Systems: The Journal of Systems Consultation and Management* **4** 198–200.

## Endnotes

[1] The editors owe this example to Martin Aldred, one of the trainers for *Psychosis Revisited*.

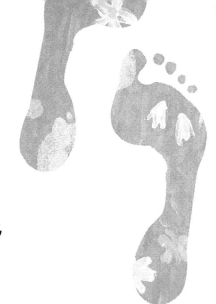

# Chapter 7

# Recovery from schizophrenia? A carer's perspective

Anonymous

Our son and other members of the family were keen not to be identified in this story, so our son's name has been changed and my account from a carer's perspective has been written anonymously. I hope that this will not detract from the reader's experience of the chapter. In every other respect, the story is factual. I am writing about recovery from the perspective of a carer. How different might this be to the perspective of an individual suffering from schizophrena? You decide.

## Early days

The story begins with Anthony at university. Anthony was the least academically inclined of our four children. His three older sisters progressed through further education and were on the way towards professions. He was keen to follow them and many of his peer group from college where he had gained a merit in a BTEC Business Studies qualification. At university he obtained an HND in business studies but at some cost to his health as a result of the various excesses of student life and being away from home for the first time.

Nonetheless, he did feel able now to pursue his chosen career in marketing. In many respects, Anthony's character and personality lent itself to this area as he was more of an extrovert than his siblings, with a great sense of humour and always a witty phrase or two to get himself out of trouble or to avoid domestic duties.

He secured a job with an American computer company selling software and IT equipment in a telesales office. This proved to be very competitive, high-pressure selling with the ringing of bells when a sale was achieved. Anthony woke one Monday morning after a few weeks of this and was in a very troubled state and unable to set foot outside. The taxi that was waiting to take him to the station was sent away. Anthony spent that day and many others on the settee in an emotional and tearful turmoil. It is still distressing for his family some 10 years on to imagine how he must have been feeling or what on earth was going on that morning. His GP suggested he had been on drugs during the weekend but this was not the case. Arrangements were made for a visit from a community psychiatric nurse (CPN). The CPN totally ignored us, (Anthony's parents), and came and went without saying a word to us despite the obvious shock and confusion that we were facing at that time.

## His family/carers

It is still really difficult to express how we were affected by this turn of events. We were, or so we thought, a perfectly normal professional family with four happy, healthy grown up youngsters all progressing towards or already into adulthood with stable secure futures ahead. Then suddenly like a bolt out of the blue, a severe mental illness struck one member of the family. The feelings of confusion and anxiety at this stage were very strong. We spent months in a state of shock as we became more aware of the seriousness of his illness. We had no explanation or support. This was magnified many times by the sense that there was something wrong with us and our family to have a son suffering in this way. Our confusion was of course linked to the stigma that prevails around mental ill health.

It was very difficult for his sisters as well; although they had left home at this stage they were frequent visitors but the fun of popping in disappeared as for months we were totally preoccupied by Anthony's illness and could talk about little else. Inevitably, they called less frequently; we lost touch with many of our friends as we didn't have the enthusiasm for making the effort to meet up. For a long time we were not keen to let on what was happening. We, as his carers, were still not receiving any help in understanding Anthony's illness. There appeared to be no help available for us either as we tried to deal with the sense of loss and distress and the feelings of guilt that we were experiencing ourselves. The stigma, attached to mental illness at that time and still continuing today, made it very difficult for us to discuss the problem with anyone outside our immediate family.

This was not helped by the suggestion from the CPN that the parents/family were part of the problem and not the solution. We felt very much excluded from the ensuing processes at least in the early stages. We, as his carers received absolutely no help in dealing with the trauma that we were experiencing at this time. This made it more difficult for us to provide the most effective help for Anthony.

## Onset of schizophrenia

Over the next two or so years, Anthony received a lot of treatment from the local psychiatric services. He was prescribed high levels of medication for what was diagnosed at that time as anxiety and depression. After some time he began to respond to the treatment and his mental health began to improve. This continued for some time to the extent that the psychiatrist began to reduce his medication. It is a continuing regret that this progressive reduction was carried out too quickly and Anthony suffered a severe relapse. This was not recognised and dealt with very quickly. As a result, what later became diagnosed as schizophrenia, hit Anthony with a serious deterioration in his condition. We still feel guilty that in 2000/01 we did not spot and take action as this deterioration occurred.

With my wife approaching retirement I also arranged to retire early. These plans were well advanced when we began to ask what the purpose of this was, as our quality of life at this time at home was really poor. Anthony was living at home and was at a very low point in his illness with daily visits to the day treatment centre at the local mental health hospital. He was hearing voices and was disturbed when watching television.

## New GP and psychiatric team

It was only some time after our move to an adjacent town that Anthony's care was moved to a new GP and psychiatric team. From then on we experienced a whole new side to the NHS and discovered that there were other services available to help those suffering from mental illness, and for their carers. We became aware for the first time of the care plan approach (CPA) and a new excellent CPN became his key worker, a role we had not come across until that time. She managed to secure Anthony's confidence and motivate him to move forwards. Anthony had always been very compliant, taking his medication and trying anything that was suggested to him that would help him towards recovery.

## Our own understanding of mental illness

We now became more involved in the care and treatment of Anthony. We were also referred to the support worker from Rethink who gave us the most amazing help and advice on how to help Anthony. We were enrolled on the Carers' Education and Support Programme (CESP), which was run by Rethink. This involved 10 half-days and was an invaluable help for us in coming to terms with the feelings of guilt and the sense of loss we were experiencing. It also helped us to understand better the nature of mental illness and the medication for its treatment. Most importantly, we learned how we could help ourselves and the ones we cared for to proceed towards some recovery.

We were introduced to the carers needs assessment process, which again we were not aware of until that time. This looks at what help and support the carers themselves need in order to be more effective in their role as carers, and to maintain their own health and lead normal lives. These assessments are now a statutory entitlement and show how the pivotal role of the carer has become recognised as being of paramount importance in the successful treatment of the mentally ill person.

Our introduction to Rethink gave us a whole new expectation for ourselves. After some six years of struggle we could not believe this would be possible.

## Progress towards recovery – for him

Gradually, the improvement began to take place and with the help of an excellent organisation, Move to Independence, Anthony moved out from home and into shared accommodation and over the next few years progressed to the current situation where he now has a one bedroom council flat a couple of miles from our home. As part of the Move to Independence arrangements, he was allocated a care worker who was superb and took a lot of the responsibility for his care away from us. She helped Anthony to begin to manage his affairs, to shop and to learn to cook for himself. This gave him a life more independent of his parents and much more normal for a 32-year-old. It also gave us the opportunity to begin reclaiming our own lives.

## Progress towards recovery – for us

This whole new approach has given us, as Anthony's carers, some degree of recovery. We have come a long way towards accepting the reality of Anthony's and our own situation but my wife particularly still finds it very painful to talk about what has happened, how it has destroyed Anthony's life and the inevitable damage it has done to our own. I have become more accepting of the situation and found some recovery in sharing our experiences with others and helping those in similar situations to ourselves to realise that there is hope. With the right help and support, things do improve and life becomes more acceptable. I have for the last four years been involved in a carers' strategy group at the local mental health hospital helping to ensure that the carers are properly included in the treatment of those suffering from severe mental illness. I am also a member of the advisory group for service users and carers for the Doctorate of Clinical Psychology training course at the local university. This group helps to ensure that the trainees understand what it is like to be a carer for someone suffering from mental illness and learn to involve both service users and carers as colleagues in their future role as clinical psychologists.

## What it's like now – for him

As a result of the medication, Anthony no longer suffers the main symptoms of schizophrenia. Nevertheless, his quality of life is severely impaired, particularly when compared with that of his siblings and his former peer group at college. He finds it very difficult to manage his day-to-day affairs and has struggled to get and hold on to any meaningful work. This is not helped by the regulations under the benefits system. The permitted work rules restrict the number of hours he can work in a week to less than 16 and a maximum income currently of £93.50 per week – with a corresponding reduction in his income support. A year or two ago when doing some temporary work, Anthony exceeded these limits in one week and his income support was immediately stopped and it took me five months to get it reinstated and then only after some help from the local MP. He has had no meaningful long-term work since then. Much more research is needed in this area. More flexible rules would have helped Anthony to test the water in a move back into work and this may perhaps have led to a more fulfilled life than he currently experiences.

Anthony has always struggled to accept his diagnosis and still needs a lot more care than he is prepared to admit in the general management of his affairs and particularly in relation to getting work. Regrettably, he has for years felt unable to engage with those who might perhaps be able to help him in this area. In particular, he does not want to explain to prospective employers and agencies why his work history is so patchy. Equally, his perception of what he is able to achieve and the sort of job that he could apply for is way beyond what could be reasonably expected in the light of his condition at the present time and his employment history. However, it is a measure of his recovery that he has ambition and would like to have meaningful employment. In the past weeks, he has begun to engage with a service that provides volunteer work for those recovering from mental ill health. We are very encouraged by this change in his approach and hope it might lead eventually to more constructive work opportunities. He has also begun work for a local pizza delivery chain and works two or three evenings as a delivery driver.

## What it's like now – for us

After two years with the Move to Independence team, Anthony's allocated care worker moved on and the full responsibility for his care reverted to us. This happened without much notice, which we found very difficult and stressful. It was as though the whole burden for his care was being placed back on our shoulders. Anthony continues to need considerable support from us with the day-to-day events of life, from dealing with his finances and general admin, to shopping and housekeeping, for example. Left to his own devices his finances become a nightmare. For me with my accounting background this has been especially difficult as I have found it hard to accept that anyone could have such problems dealing with what seems to me to be so obvious and straightforward – what comes in has to be managed so that it covers what has to go out!

With his co-operation, I have coped with this by rearranging his banking arrangements. His benefits are paid into an account – over which he has no control and this money is kept to pay his standing orders and direct debits with the remainder being paid into a day-to-day account for his food shopping and personal expenditure. He manages this account well and there are no longer major issues with there being nothing left to pay his direct debits for utilities, phones, insurance etc. For years this created endless grief and stress both for himself and for us. Anthony had great difficulty managing his bank account, often having direct debits and standing orders returned, with repeated charges for exceeding overdrafts, which should never have been granted to him in the first place. Amounts paid in penalties and charges (mostly funded by us) were reclaimed and after a rather long-winded process some £1,300 was refunded by his bank.

For years Anthony had his own car. In many respects this was good for him because it gave him more independence but he never had sufficient income to fund its cost. There arose continual problems of parking charges, clamping and tow-away charges, to say nothing of repairs required as a result of the lack of water or oil, and the emergency rescues from running out of petrol. When he was disqualified from driving for 20 months for a drink/driving offence perversely, once we were over the shock, it proved to be a relief for us financially and the catalyst for a major reduction in stress. We were much less anxious about where he was, particularly late at night.

Many problems arise from a lack of clarity in his decision-making processes. There are many examples of this. On a couple of occasions recently, the pilot light on his boiler had gone out, leaving him in the middle of winter with no heating. He had remained in the cold for days rather than let us know or put in a call himself to the local authority repairs team – even though we had met up with him in the meantime.

We have provided him with a pay-as-you-go mobile and keep the credits topped up for him. Yet so often he allows the battery to run out and it could be days before he will plug it in to recharge it. This is such an important means for him to keep in contact with us and for us with him. Often we arrange to meet up and he will forget the time or place and will not have the mobile with him. How frustrating this is for all of us!

We sort out his prescriptions each month because otherwise it just would not happen. Experience shows that he would run out long before he would get around to arranging some more and this could have pretty serious consequences.

# Summary

There has undoubtedly been some recovery for us as we have made more of a life for ourselves. However, the emotional stress and the endless involvement with the day-to-day affairs of Anthony's life and worries about his future continue to affect us. He is never far from our thoughts no matter what we try and do for ourselves. As Anthony's health has improved it has become more frustrating that he seems unable to cope effectively with the basics of life, like shopping, cleaning, cooking, washing up, opening his own post and dealing with the day-to-day admin and simple chores. The lack of support and help in the early years made it impossible for us to begin the process of recovery and most importantly to be able to recognise the deteriorating situation in Anthony's condition in 2000/01. There is no doubt that later on being fully involved in Anthony's care programme, having an excellent CPN and with access to other agencies like Rethink, has made an enormous difference to our lives and how we are able to help Anthony in his own process of recovery.

# Conclusion

While all of us have responded to the better help available to us in recent years and have experienced some recovery, I would have to admit that each of us has further to go. We cannot envisage a time when we will get back to the sort of life we expected for ourselves and our family before the onset of mental illness. However, we have recovered to the extent that we have each reclaimed some part of our lives.

With recent very small reductions in his medication, Anthony has been given encouragement and although the lack of work prospects holds him back, he often feels reasonably accepting and comfortable with his life. It helps us knowing that he is feeling better and with all the help we have received we are making a life for ourselves too.

Finally, it is undoubtedly a fact that the proper and full involvement of the carers improves the recovery prospects both for the one suffering from the mental illness and for the carers themselves.

### Some thoughts on good practice

- Over the past 10 years our experience of the way carers are treated was sometimes awful and at other times really good. This has shown us that proper and meaningful involvement of the carers in the treatment of those suffering from mental ill health improves the outcome for both the person they care for and themselves.

- There is much that is good about the services provided by the NHS and a lot has been done to ensure that carers are involved but more is needed. Mental health professionals involved in the training of other professionals should teach them (and be prepared to learn from them) good practice in relation to meaningful carer involvement.

- All mental health professionals should build relationships with some of the many voluntary bodies/charities (like Rethink) who do such a fabulous job in helping carers come to terms with, understand and live with mental ill health in the family.

- Recovery is a misunderstood notion. Recovery to what? Can the life of the service user be improved – yes, definitely. But can someone who has suffered severe mental illness get back to the way they were before (which is what 'recovery' is in my terms) – no, I don't think so. The best that can be hoped for is some stability and 'a fulfilment' subject to all the limitations. For Anthony, life has improved and he is better by miles than he was five years ago – but when compared with his peers and his siblings his life is terrible – and from time to time he is very aware of this. What we have to do, with the help of the professionals is help him to reach his potential – accepting that this is now at a much lower level than might formerly have been the case.

- Much needs to be done to make the benefits system more flexible so that those recovering from severe mental illness have a more realistic and less penal way of getting back into employment. It is essential that the frontline staff with their contacts help carers to navigate the hugely complex benefits system for those they care for.

## Chapter 8

# Lying on a mattress on the floor

Moira Green

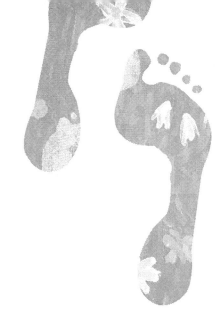

I am a family-orientated mother of two daughters, and have participated in the *Psychosis Revisited* training over the last six years. My involvement with this training has allowed me to understand and accept my psychotic episodes, regain control of my life and increase my confidence. I am also a former member of the Capital project.

Lying on a mattress on the floor, covered by one blanket that had a large hole in it, unable to imagine the horrors I was about to encounter, I finally convinced myself to open my eyes and face the world. Looking around in a daze, I was surprised to see the lack of hygiene and care in this room, nothing but coldness surrounded me. I noticed that there was blood on the wall, which I hoped was from a previous occupant and the window had no curtains except a piece of material hanging on by a thread. Opening my eyes fully, I noticed three men just standing, staring at me lying on the floor. *'Shut my door'* I asked the two people sitting outside, I have got no privacy in here. *'No'* was their reply. *'Can I go outside?'*. *'No'* was the reply. *'Can I use the telephone?'*. *'No'* again. This continued on and on. *'Can I see my children today?'*

What had I done to deserve this treatment only nine days after giving birth? Sitting up on my mattress I noticed that my locker had gone; this contained everything that I had owned and was precious to me, especially my small bit of change I had kept to use the telephone to speak to my children. I asked how long I had been out and they said about 16 hours. I began to recall what had happened to me previously to this.

## First admission

My daughter was born in 1991 and I suffered post-natal elation due to a very emotional pregnancy. I was given the rubella injection and told by my GP to not try for a baby for one month. I was already helping to nurse my nephew with cerebral palsy. I was very fortunate to have conceived after eight weeks and attended the first scan at 13-weeks pregnant. It was explained to me, in not very kind words, that my GP had misinformed me and that the safe period was three months. I was offered to be booked in for a termination or alternatively wait until the 22-week scan to see if my baby had arms and legs and then decide. To my horror, I was told at 22 weeks, you have to give birth to the baby anyway. What would I have done if this had affected my baby, would I have been left to feel like a murderer? What a decision to make. I continued to do my nephew's exercises only to watch him suffer up to 16 fits a day and constantly asked myself and my husband, could we be as strong as Isaac's fantastic parents?

We decided to proceed with the pregnancy and fortunately I delivered a healthy 7lb 1oz baby girl. I was amazed and shocked that this had happened because towards the end of the pregnancy, I had convinced myself that my baby would be severely handicapped with *'sprigs for arms and sprigs for legs'*, to quote the doctor who was offering me the abortion. I did not want to put my perfect new baby down. I would have held her in my arms for the rest of her life if I could have. I was discharged after giving the hospital permission to take blood from myself and my daughter to be sent to London for research into rubella in pregnancy.

I was very happy to return back to the family home. However, I was becoming unwell and not looking after myself, as my only concerns were for Siobhan. I was not eating, sleeping or resting. I remember my husband saying to people as they left, I am not sure what is happening as she is behaving weird. Being from a family with no history of mental health problems, and no member of the family ever being admitted to a psychiatric hospital, this was all new for everyone concerned. Eventually the GP was called and she then requested a home visit from a psychiatrist. To my horror, I could hear this very rude lady asking my husband very personal questions about my childhood, ie. had I ever been physically or sexually abused by a member of my family? Little did I realise that that was the start of me becoming invisible. How dare she ask somebody these questions about me, why not speak to me, instead of speaking about me, around me? I was given some tablets to take. It was never discussed with me what my diagnoses were, what the symptoms of the problem were or even what the name of the medication was or possible side effects (very important when you feel vulnerable anyway).

I became very unwell and was admitted to a psychiatric hospital. I was told by the social worker in my home that it was a normal general hospital because I was physically unwell. I cannot begin to describe the fear. It was explained to me that I was unable to leave the hospital without the permission of my newly appointed psychiatrist. I would have to take all the medications given to me and then maybe I could go home. At this point, looking back, I realise that I was elated, although I find it strange that my normal behaviour prior to giving birth, I would now say was elation. I have always lived a fast and quick life but this was not asked by the psychiatrist. I was only in for a few days and sent home. I returned back to work when Siobhan was six weeks old and stopped all the medication and returned back to 'normal' or as normal as could be expected with the support of my family and other close friends. I cannot really recall a lot about this episode.

## Here we go again

Trying to deny all the maternal feeling for wanting another child was becoming too much for me. Eventually, after a long chat with my husband, we both agreed to let nature take its course. Within three months I was pregnant again, however, this baby was miscarried. I again let nature decide for me and only eight weeks after my miscarriage, I was pregnant again. I was delighted as everyone else was, especially Siobhan, but at the back of my mind laid fear. Within the first few weeks, my fears began to grow as I was experiencing some unusual discharge. I immediately visited my GP who took a vaginal swab and a week later gave me the all clear. This problem continued throughout my pregnancy and I was convincing myself that the baby had died inside me and this is why I still had the ongoing problem. I continued giving swabs only to receive the all clear each time. Seven swabs later and at 41-weeks pregnant, I was casually told I had Strep B. I was given antibiotics and told the baby would need to go into intensive care and have a screening. This meant nothing to me and was never explained. Just as an afterthought the doctor mentioned that if the baby was to swallow any of the infection on delivery then she could die. On a visit to an antenatal appointment (which I had made myself to discuss the chances of the post-natal illness happening again), I explained to the doctor (who was swinging on his chair from side to side and tapping the table with his pen) about my previous problems and the post-natal elation I had suffered. He looked and me and said '*I think you have it wrong – it's called post-natal depression*'. We continued for about five minutes with me saying '*No, elation*', him replying '*depression*'. I was getting very agitated and then he opened up my file and said '*Don't worry, I have written you up for a shot of antidepressants when you deliver*'. To this day, I am unaware if I ever received this.

I delivered a baby girl 7lb 11oz, Alicia. I was told to breastfeed as she would need the antibodies in the breast milk. I was lying in a side room alone when two nurses appeared in green suits and masks and asked to take Alicia to intensive care. I was told I could not go with her as she had to have a lumbar puncture done and it is best if parents are not present as it is very distressful. I was taken to the ward and decided to take a bath to take my mind off things. I had just stepped out the bath and a nurse advised that a midwife from intensive care needed to see me. They explained that Alicia was on medication and had the lumbar puncture done and X-rays of her chest to see if she had swallowed any of the infection. She then presented me with a Polaroid picture of Alicia. '*What is this for?*' I asked. '*Oh, it's for you in case she dies.*'

Again, I returned home and was on iron tablets and feeling very weak, but mentally well. My mother had come over from north Wales to help me adjust to the new member of the family. I was becoming very irritable and the GP was called – I had a temperature of 103 and needed some antibiotics. She discussed my well-being and felt I needed to go to a psychiatric hospital again. I agreed to go as there were a lot of problems in the home surrounding my husband's affair, which I had just discovered and felt hospital might be a good option. I was upset as the mental health team explained to me that there was no mother and baby unit available due to lack of money (another favourite saying from professionals). I found it very intimidating to have so many people in my house telling me what to do, eg. community nurse, GP, psychiatrist and sometimes the police. I watched as Alicia was fed her first bottle and was upset that she was unable to keep it down. Why can't I keep her with me and feed her, I thought. Why should I have to break the bond and be separated from her? I felt so angry and disappointed at the lack of services that were being offered to me again. Holding her in my arms and saying goodbye was soul destroying. I had fought so hard for her to arrive safe and now at nine days old I had to let her go. I wanted to know and experience a newborn baby. This was my second chance at it and here it was being taken away. Handing her to my sister and brother-in law was a very comforting decision, as my sister was actually present when Alicia had been born and both her and her husband had taken on Siobhan when I was in hospital. Siobhan was very confused as any three-year-old child would be, as she went off to Auntie Barb's and Uncle Dave's.

I was extremely lucky to have such kind people in my life. Siobhan had attended nursery run by a friend of the family and she had attended this since six weeks old. I had agreed with Mary and Joe who ran the nursery that I would return back to work after Alicia's birth and pay them then. However, being sectioned in the hospital did not allow me to return to work and, years later, I discovered she was allowed to continue to go to nursery, even though I had not paid my friends. Mary and Joe continue to allow Siobhan to go to nursery for no fee. I questioned Mary about this and she replied that what Siobhan needed was stability in her life and this also allowed Barbara to go to work as well.

## Second admission

Upon admission to the same mixed ward, (again I cannot believe that there are such wards) I saw and heard patients actually having sexual intercourse in the bed next to mine. I cannot believe that when people suffer elation and their sex drive increases, the NHS put males and females together in this way! I was given strong medication to make me sleep. Waking up, I felt the same fear as before and could hear a lot of noise and commotion on the ward. I decided to stay in the room and collect my thoughts. Unfortunately, or fortunately, I can remember most of the details of this admission. I can recall coming out of my room one day and asking staff to help me as I was feeling very unwell. I was still under midwifery care and should have still been under the care of a midwife if I was at home but for some reason this was overlooked. The fact that I needed to wear a sanitary towel was pointed out to me. Dazed by all the strong medication, I went to the canteen area and one of my fellow patients shouted '*you have blood all over your pyjama bottoms!*' I am very angry and upset about having to suffer the indignity – I always say I can recover from the puerperal psychosis but not from the loss of my dignity.

Eventually, I was taken over to the maternity hospital, which I gave birth in, for yet another high vaginal swab to be taken. This was about 16 days after giving birth. The midwife who was attending me looked very concerned as she realised that I had mastitis in both breasts and said I had a fever as well. She began to shout at the nurse who had taken me over and asked why has she been left in this state for so long? I was given an antibiotic and a breast pump to release my milk. I returned to the ward with this in a bucket for some reason and the staff outside the room took it off me to see what it was. They all began to laugh and make comments such as, '*Go on Daisy the cow – get in your room and be milked!*' I put my dressing gown over the back of the door to cover up the peep hole and a male member of staff barged in and said, '*you cannot do that*'. I asked for a private room to express my milk and he laughed and said, '*just get on with it*'. I sat on the bed and cried with embarrassment for being made to feel so degraded.

I asked for my daughters to be brought in to visit me as I longed to cuddle them. The reply was that there were very violent males on the ward and we cannot risk the children being harmed. I asked, '*Why can't I go in the family room then?*' They all laughed, '*because we haven't got one*'. Alicia was being looked after by a social services nanny, Pam, who had been appointed to help out. I would call her and ask to see Alicia. '*Ok*', she would reply, only then for the ward to call her and refuse her permission to bring the children in. I was never told of this and would sit and wait all day long thinking it was the nanny holding back the visit. I would ring her the next day and accuse her of keeping my baby away from me.

## Is this really a hospital?

I was experiencing very violent mood swings and would be elated in the morning then very depressed by evening. The medication was very powerful and frightening to take, especially without any explanation from anyone. I never did see a pharmacist on the wards. I would go to the food area for the evening tea after medication has been passed out and see people giving medication out of their mouths to waiting drug dealers, and for this they would receive £10 cash. I was offered a bag of heroin, crack, cocaine and other drugs, I had never even seen before. I was told by these so called visitors that this will get you better quicker than the drugs off the trolley and, being so vulnerable, I don't know how I resisted. I have never touched any drugs in my life and being so anti-drugs is what helped me. I informed a member of the staff of what was going on and they said yes we know but we cannot physically search visitors under the Human Rights Act. What about my human rights? What about the rights of my children?

I was feeling that I would never get better and would cry for hours with frustration. *'When will I get better?'* I would ask again and again. *'Time'* was the reply. This made me very upset because I wanted it now. I took all the medication given to me but I found it very hard to sleep at night because my brain could not stop. I would have endless conversations with myself and eventually have to get out of bed to try and talk to somebody to allow the thoughts to come out of my mouth. I tried to talk to a member of staff who aggressively put me back to bed and ordered me to stay there until the morning. Needless to say, I kept getting up about 6.30 in the morning; I was given a sleeping pill to allow me to rest and hopefully get some sleep. Cuddled up in my bed trying to escape the torture of not being in control of my own brain, I was forcefully pulled onto my feet and placed in a chair in the TV room. *'Stay there, you are not sleeping today when you have kept me up all night on my night shift.'* The nurse was doing a double shift and would not allow me to sleep in my bed. If she noticed I had closed my eyes she would hit me to wake me up. I was becoming more and more aggressive and felt I had to fight for my rights. I was very elated this time and can remember walking around and around in circles (like a mad dog) and was constantly asking numerous members of staff if I could go out onto the field. *'No'* was the reply.

Things not making sense – two and two making five – is a very confusing way to live. I began to smell things nobody else could. I also began to see things nobody else could. I had a lot of fear going to the dining area as there had been lots of fighting between the male patients. I sat next to a man who had just put a pork chop on his plate, I could smell the stench of dry blood coming from the plate and, thinking I was doing him a favour, I picked the plate up and proceeded to scrape his only meal into the bin. He stood up and punched me full force in the face and I got taken to my room with no meal and lots of privileges stopped. Sitting in my room and reflecting on why I had behaved in this way made me understand that I was flitting in and out of my body, somehow sharing it with this illness. I was only allowed about half the day in my body and then I could physically feel the illness stepping in. I imagine this is like being possessed. I would like to point out that in the psychotic state I did, 100% believe the feelings I was experiencing. I became obsessed that the staff at the hospital where trying to poison me so I refused to eat or drink. I became very weak physically as I was trying to recover from giving birth.

## Not at the moment Moira

I now understand the pattern leading up to the state of psychosis – it was the most frightening experience of my life. I became very unwell very fast and lived in a parallel world. I became deluded and believed that I was the Virgin Mary. I used to go from person to person in the hospital hoping somebody would confirm this. Now I understand that due to my life being so empty, feeling worthless and having nothing of value and losing my children, husband and home etc. I had to reinvent a person of importance ie. the Virgin Mary.

Asking to see the children was a daily occurrence from me. However, every time I approached the staff, even before I spoke, I would hear 'Not at the moment Moira'. I got so upset from hearing this I tried to turn this into a joke, so off I went to the OT group and designed myself a name badge with 'Not at the moment Moira' on it. I was so unwell that I lost the ability to write. I had to be reintroduced to colours via colouring in. I was sectioned, and felt very lonely and isolated. I had previously contacted Pam to bring in the children and again they had not showed. I picked up my shoes and put them on without anybody noticing. I got as close to the doors as possible and thought if you won't bring them to me then I will go to them. I managed just to get to the other side of the doors when all the alarm bells started to ring. Before I knew where I was, I was pinned on the floor by about six staff. I was kept there until the corridor was emptied. The pain was unbearable; they had my hands up my back and in a thumb lock they picked me up off the floor face down while a member of staff was pulling my head up by my hair. I was thrown on a mattress on the floor with six members of staff hitting and verbally abusing me. By this time, I now realised that I was becoming psychotic and had, the previous day, seen the Devil standing in my room. I was struggling to keep my trousers on as they were saying, 'go on Damian stick it in her arse' (Damian was the name of my nurse and also the name of the antichrist in the Omen films, and having a nurse called this was very frightening). The struggle had become by this time a gang rape in my mind, as I was shouting and screaming for help, nobody came. This is where I find me lying on a mattress on the floor.

## Someone to listen

Looking back it is very upsetting that a lot of my anxiety and fears could have been kept at bay by just a bit of communication from the professionals, eg. explanations about the procedure of being sectioned and the medication I was being forced to take. The loss of control of my life was hard to accept. I just needed somebody to put down the paperwork and have a one-to-one chat with me, somebody to care for me like a human being. It was about six weeks into my admission when I discovered that the nurses were, in fact, not prison wardens like I'd thought. I was upset as I thought that nurses had to have nursing qualities (kind, caring, compassionate). All of this I had not witnessed.

One member of staff said he would sign me and another patient (who was also elated) out and take us for a run. Against all advice he took us out, wow, I am sitting smiling now remembering the feeling of release. It was great just allowing all that excess energy to burn off. He was puffed out trying to keep up with us shouting 'you are sectioned – slow down!' He said he enjoyed seeing the difference it made to us – plus the other patient and I had a good night's sleep. I know that there are many fantastic psychiatric professionals out there and I am not criticising you all – just most of the staff I met at the time. I was eventually offered a drug called lithium, which made my moods stable but I had to have a blood test every three months for toxicity levels. This made me very anxious as the same people who examined my seven week swabs would also be checking the blood levels. I felt very disappointed that my swabs were clear when I did actually have Strep B. I was forced to take the lithium but am very glad that it eventually worked for me.

## Making sense of the madness

I was discharged from the hospital about three months later and went to stay with my parents in north Wales. I was on my own without the girls and was very depressed at this time, as my mood had eventually subsided from elation. It was hard work for my parents as I remember having suicidal thoughts. I was looking forward to getting Siobhan back but very apprehensive about 'that *baby!*' I asked my dad to go to Liverpool and bring back Siobhan for me and he just looked and said, '*no, you have two kids not one.*' I was very angry at the time and thought you don't understand what I am going through. Little did I know that he had acknowledged my fears and was trying to help me overcome them. He was right; I am very grateful to my parents for their help and support. I had a fantastic childhood provided by both my mum and dad and feel that none of my childhood experiences contributed to my mental breakdown in any way.

The churning inside my stomach was uncontrollable, feelings of anticipation mixed in with total excitement not knowing how to cope with the next hurdle in my life, bonding with my baby. It was very strange to feel scared of your own child but prior to this moment Alicia's needs had been attended to by other people, not me. I didn't know how much she ate, slept, or how much milk she drank. I picked her up from her grandmother and sat with her and Siobhan on the trip back to Wales. I started to feel claustrophobic and scared that I couldn't cope with this; trying to deal with a severe mental illness was hard enough. I fed Alicia her bottle and started to feel the same way any mother would when she first holds her newborn baby. Thankfully, this was the start of the slow process to bond with my baby. My relationship with Siobhan had suffered in other ways – she was physically removed from my body by her feet on the ward as they said dinner was due. She vomited outside the hospital and was unable to move for half an hour. This was only told to me by the social worker years later.

Things continued to go from bad to worse. I returned home with the children and had to face up to the fact that my husband was having an affair. I got no follow-up services (in January I was told there were no more funds available until April). I continued to see the Devil on numerous occasions at home and I asked for help. I was told by the GP to get in touch with the Post-Natal Association in London, yet this came to nothing. I wanted and needed to make sense of this tragic event so I contacted the hospital and asked to speak to somebody. The ward manager agreed to see me and it was a life saver for me and so my road to recovery began. She answered lots of my weird questions about my behaviour. I explained that I felt I was treated like an animal and that is why I behaved like one.

Eventually I split up from my husband, became elated and was admitted to hospital again. This admission was not as bad as the last one. I made the decision to leave my husband, and my sister Linda kindly offered for me to live with her. I am extremely grateful for her kindness and support through the worst part of my life. I used to pick the children up from the matrimonial home where he had moved in his woman. I was taken to court on 19 December 1996 and lost custody of the children due to my husband using my mental health problems against me. I was facing a Christmas without my children and, at this point, suicide seemed like a very good option. I just wanted to escape the pain but not forever. However, I managed to turn this around and get angry with myself for bringing two beautiful girls into this world and then leaving them. I had a fantastic mother growing up and realised how important I would be to them. I looked inside myself for inner strength and luckily found it, and allowed it to grow. The children did return to me in July 1998 and their father died in September 1998. I have continued to stay well and my last admission to hospital was back in July 1997 when that woman (my husband's girlfriend) gave birth to their son.

## Looking back

It is confusing to explain my recovery as I feel each day I am still learning to recover and live with this diagnosis of bipolar affective disorder. Again my sense of humour takes over when friends ask what it means. I simply reply that I have an allergy to polar bears. I can remember when I was allowed home on day release and considered that an overdose of tablets was my only way out of this awful situation. I put the girls to bed (only three years old and nine months) and went downstairs to get a drink to take all the pills I had gathered from around the house. I crept into the girls' bedroom to say goodbye and sat on the floor, just listening to them breathing I realised how selfish of me this would be, and just how important my mum had been to me in my life. I remember crying from a part of me deep inside I didn't know existed and asked for help from anybody who was listening. I begged for some inner strength to allow me to continue without being able to see the end.

I am convinced to this day that this was a major turning point in my life. I continued to take one day at a time and not worry too much about what the future holds. Today I still feel a pang of guilt. I wonder what would have come of my beautiful daughters as their father passed away when they were three and six years old. I could have chosen a life for them as orphans at such a small age. I only reflect on this when I talk about the past for my work as a service user trainer.

I was very lucky to have fantastic support from my family and friends. I met Pam, who was the nanny appointed by social services and also her two children, Paul and Shelly, who supported me through this illness much more than what was expected and have since become very good friends of mine. They still support me to this day. For example, Paul telephoned me to see how I was. '*Not too good*' I replied, '*Why?*' he asked. '*I have been up since 5.00am washing windows this morning,*' I replied. He said, '*Why didn't you ring me and say because I would have drove down and got you,*' and I answered '*Ah, do you love me that much?*' '*No*' Paul said, '*the windows in the conservatory are dirty!*' '*Thank you Paul.*'

I find it very difficult and embarrassing after being so unwell to cope with people's attitudes, so being from Liverpool, I decided that if I can laugh at myself, when other people do it, then it won't hurt. I have received numerous postcards with donkeys on them and also had a good laugh with Mark Hayward, the clinical psychologist, when I got lost trying to find my way to Guildford University and ended up in the Guildford Cathedral instead.

I realise lots of stress can bring on an episode so I try to live as stress free a life as possible (hard task with two teenage daughters!). I am very aware of my early warning signs as is my partner and act on them accordingly. I am aware that the illness lives alongside of me and sometimes will try and catch up with me. I decided to move to West Sussex as I felt we should not live in the past and a fresh start would be good for us all. I have another kind sister who lives down here and this allowed me to sell up and move in with her until I could find myself a house. I have met some lovely people along the way, especially my partner Kevin, who is very kind, caring and understanding. After six weeks into the relationship, I decided to tell Kevin about my bipolar affective disorder and give him the chance to end the relationship if he wanted. He simply got a lot of information off the internet, which we discussed and seven years later are both still together and very happy.

I would like to say a big thank you to Siobhan and Alicia for helping me along the way, being so kind and honest with me – no secrets are important for us all and have allowed our feelings to move on. I can remember Siobhan when she was about seven years old asking why I was taken to that funny hospital. I replied, '*I just sometimes need to sleep as I go a bit too fast*'. Alicia looked confused and piped up, '*Does that mean that our cat has mental health problems because he runs around the house too fast and runs up the curtains and jumps off?'* I have always been honest and answered the questions as they have arisen and the girls are very respectful of my illness.

I felt it a very important part of my recovery that I had a diagnosis. Once I received this, I could go to the library and read about puerperal psychosis and what its effects had on my personality. I now understand the bizarre behaviour I displayed and what psychosis means. I was extremely poorly for about three weeks when I experienced the psychosis. It meant a lot to understand that the illness made me behave in that way and I was not in control of this, I sometimes feel very embarrassed that people had to see me in this condition and again can only laugh about it and turn it into a joke if it is ever discussed with people who witnessed it. I also believe humour helps them to deal with it in this way too.

## Moving forward

I fully respect my illness and live a lifestyle to keep it at bay. I don't drink, smoke or take any illegal drugs. I know what my early warning signs are, lack of sleep, fast speech, excessive cleaning etc., and my partner is very aware of them and will suggest I go to the GP for some olanzapine. This has resulted in not being admitted to hospital in the last 11 years. Upon moving to West Sussex, I met a lady called Anne Beales who was then the Director of Capital (service users' organisation) and Anne allowed my confidence to grow; when she thought I was ready, she encouraged me to start presenting. My first presentation was back in 2003 and I feel my confidence and understanding has grown so much in the past five years. Attending these training sessions and meeting the staff has allowed me to make sense of the other side of the story. Now that I understand the difficulties around working in an acute psychiatric hospital with all the pressure it brings, this has allowed me, in turn, to accept but not agree with lots of my treatment. I have built up relationships with professionals on a personal level and have broken down my own barrier of us and them. Also, it has allowed me to be able to trust people in authority. Being sectioned is such a frightening experience because you lose control of your life and a professional is in charge of it.

Over the last five years, I have often been asked by participants of the *Psychosis Revisited* workshops if I wish I had never experienced this illness. I wish the first few months of my children's life was not missed and I also wish I did not receive the treatment in the way I did, but lying on that mattress on the floor made me so determined to not allow this to win and I promised myself that day that I would make a positive experience of this mess. I can actually honestly say that I have had my life enriched by this experience and have met a lot of lovely people along the way and this is what makes me who I am today.

My final saying, which kept me sane was:

**You can take away my dignity but not my sense of humour.**

### Some thoughts on good practice

- A midwife to come into my home to enable me to stay with the children.
- A mother and baby unit on the ward.
- Not being placed on a mixed sex ward. It was frightening at the time and resulted in untrue rumours about me.
- Medication and procedures like sectioning to be explained to alleviate anxiety and fear of the unknown.

- When I am experiencing psychosis, take my fear about the Devil in the room seriously and don't leave me in that room. Keep me safe.
- Listen and accept – don't be judgmental.
- Just having someone to give me 'time' to allow the thoughts to come out. If you don't they stay in my head and grow.
- To be treated like a human being – just because I am mentally unwell does not take away that fact.
- To be spoken to and not ignored and discussed amongst others as if I were invisible in the room.
- A diagnosis is important to make sense of things, as well as explanations and aftercare. It reduces fear of the unknown.

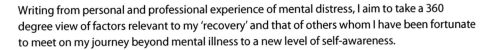

## Chapter 9

# Recovery – adventures in being

### Emma Harding

**Writing from personal and professional experience of mental distress, I aim to take a 360 degree view of factors relevant to my 'recovery' and that of others whom I have been fortunate to meet on my journey beyond mental illness to a new level of self-awareness.**

As children, many people are delightfully solipsistic and unquestioning of their position at the centre of the universe. Unfortunately, mental distress leaves many of us riddled with self-doubt, which when compounded by the relentless blasts of societal stigma that are regrettably rife, leads lots of people to shuffle shamefully into the wings of their social theatres. I have used the opportunity available in these few pages to write about my own experiences, in a cathartic way, to chart the process of exploration that led me to experiment with different facets of myself. This chapter outlines the many different ways of being that have shored up the eternal process of my recovery. I do not wish to be prescriptive and tell people how to get better, but instead to present the different ways of being that have helped me to become myself rather than the me that other people seemed to be pushing me towards. After all, 'I' am the only matter that I can, with any certainty, claim any real expertise in! I hope to outline an approach to recovery as viewing it as a series of adventures, sometimes profound, sometimes painful but always a process of self-discovery.

I could write this account from a variety of perspectives; I am a service user and a trainee clinical psychologist and I care for someone in my family who has experienced mental distress. I believe 'recovery' does not merely apply to the diminution of psychiatric symptoms; many other areas of people's lives are hurt by the experience of having a mental health problem. Relationships are often affected – with family, friends, the wider peer group and even yourself. For example, my younger brother has had to endure people in the street asking him if his *'sister [is] still a nutter?'* My family saw someone they love completely transformed from a bright, friendly girl to a brooding maelstrom of desperation, at one point close to death from a paracetamol overdose. I took 30 tablets and did not tell anybody until I realised I had been unsuccessful, four days later.

# My experiences of mental distress

I was a sometimes cheeky but generally shy, supposedly clever girl at school and my friends were surprised that on returning from my first year at university, I suddenly started dancing in strange places, describing hallucinations of alien space craft I saw overhead and sellotaping cardboard crosses to local lampposts. I had been very stressed at some massive changes in my life – going to university meant leaving the security of my home. I also came face-to-face with the uncertainty of knowledge. All I had learned during GSCEs and A levels satisfied my need for certainty; I had been working with facts. I understood facts. University studies suddenly made me aware that knowledge was generally not so cut and dried and that even what we think we do know can be easily undermined. The combination of uncertainty in my personal and social life (I felt I did not fit in with other students) combined with discovering that knowledge was no longer immutable led to the collapse of my personality. I started to hear voices, who gave me no reprieve and no privacy and I constructed elaborate belief systems to account for this new found ability. I failed my first year exams through not turning up and eventually ended up as a voluntary patient in a psychiatric ward back in the town where my parents lived. After coming out of hospital, with a fresh new diagnosis of schizophrenia, one 'friend' became terrified that I would murder someone if I did not take my medication even for a day and bemoaned the fact that 'uncontrolled schizophrenics' were roaming the streets. Another friend refused to let me child mind her son, whom she preferred to leave alone instead, and many, many more cross the street when they see me. I have learned to reframe this experience and am, of necessity, quite proud of not really being in touch with anybody I met before the age of 18 when I went to university, seeing it as a purge of unhelpful influences.

After dancing wildly in unusual places, to some extent my confidence has been tested – I have been in such embarrassing situations that it might be thought hard to get any lower. However, my 'prodromal' phase was characterised by being in social situations with people I did not know very well and being so paranoid and unsure of what to say that I clammed up and could not utter a word. My social skills were greatly diminished and I have had to try really hard not to withdraw into myself and away from others. There is now, for me a very strong sense of wanting to share my story (for my benefit more than others!) but this has often been countered by the unwillingness of others to listen, or to understand when they would entertain me. I have in turn, bored, annoyed and worried people I only know in passing, through my desire for others to hear of the earthquake that happened in my life and the terrifying depths and peaks I reached. I think this is what led to my interest in media work. After moving to London to start work as a mental health support worker, having finished my undergraduate degree, I started campaigning against stigma. This work was supported by Rethink, a mental health charity for service users and carers; I volunteered to appear on television, radio shows and in print to demonstrate that mental health problems can happen to anybody and it does not make you a monster.

Socially, I am much more confident now but I do have to rely on mantras when embarking on particularly anxiety-generating situations. Many of these were practised whilst under the care of my first clinical psychologist at a day centre near my home. I found this highly instrumental in my recovery. I spent my time revising for the exams that I had to re-sit to get back on track with my degree after a forced year out, and sewing together a stuffed toy fox. Having a strict plan and maintaining my diligence was useful, in my fragile and still rather concrete state, it was the only thing I could apply myself to. My dad tried to get me doing some exercise and would wake me at six to run round the field outside the back of the house. Though this was no doubt well intentioned, I was like many service users, a heavy smoker. This meant I puffed and panted my way around and at the end did not feel exactly much better than I had beforehand. Other similar attempts by others to make me better were usually as unwelcome although I knew they came from a good place. One much beloved family member kept asking me what I was thinking, as if this might help keep my thoughts on track.

My overdose understandably worried people, including those I had met in the first year of my undergraduate degree and I earned the nickname 'crazy Emma'. Some of these friends are still very close to me now and I am happy to say I am in a (hopefully) permanent relationship with someone I met in my undergraduate years. I had to fight to be accepted after my 'self-absorbed' descent into paranoia and have had to do lots of work on my self-esteem. Being told that everything you have thought for the last 18 months is essentially fairy dust is a humbling experience. My brain filters my contact with reality, with the world, so my reliance on it is pretty much total and hugely influential. Learning to trust it after it let me down so badly was difficult but there was no other option. One thing that genuinely helped me was medication, though finding the right one was fifth time lucky.

## Medication

No discussion of recovery would be complete without referring to medication. Some people vehemently disagree with the idea of taking medication that claims to redress problems with neurotransmitters. Craig Newnes (2000) argues that these 'chemical imbalances' are a fallacy and not proven as underlying any form of mental health problem. It certainly seems strange that whilst many people can trace their distress back to a particular life event or period, a tablet or injection can ameliorate its effects. Defining 'thought' is a tricky subject that psychologists and psychiatrists have not completely mastered. Philosophers too have not had much luck explaining the connection between mind and body. In 1637, Descartes asserted that the only thing we could ever be certain of was the statement '*I exist*' when we are actively thinking '*I exist*'. He used the snappy statement '*I think therefore I am*' (Cogito ergo sum) to demonstrate this. The principle was that any other 'knowledge' could be misdirected, or a hallucination caused by a mischievous demon. The point is that prescribing medication for a problem with emotions or thoughts should be carefully thought out as their mechanisms of change may not be transparent. Descartes' idea that our thoughts are all we can be certain of shows their importance and suggests that our bodies may be secondary. Kay Redfield Jamison distinguishes the mind/brain divide eloquently in her book, *An Unquiet Mind* (1995) and advocates psychotherapy as well as medication to soothe them both. The links between mind and brain are complex and possibly unknowable but I think therapy (not always CBT) should be offered to everyone because a 'malfunction' in the brain cannot avoid causing ripples in the psyche that it so wonderfully generates.

I am not suggesting that medication is not useful. I wholeheartedly believe that had I not had something to '*slow my thoughts down*', as my psychiatrist put it, I would not have been able to make use of the support my psychologist gave me. As a colleague at Rethink put it, medication can unlock the key to the door of recovery, but there are many rooms in the house. These 'rooms' include supportive family and romantic relationships, being free from poverty, having access to employment and having safe and stable housing, among other things.

# What is recovery?

In the midst of despair and the shattered dreams that herald the awakening of awareness that you, yes you, have a severe mental health problem, recovery seems impossible. As well as coping with the time stolen from your life by the active phase of an illness, finding the right treatment can take years. I recall sitting in a local pub with my parents, the night I was finally 'released' from hospital. I could not drink alcohol because of my frightened compliance with the instructions accompanying my medication. Though many of the other customers were my age, celebrating the end of the working week I felt distantly removed and hopeless. The gap between me and the laughing, seemingly carefree crowd was overwhelming. The world seemed five times bigger than it had when I effectively left it 18 months previously and I had to relearn several basic skills. I had to force myself into social situations and take 'baby steps'. I remember the joy I felt at learning all by myself that taking four sheets of tissue paper from the dispenser in the day hospital I went to was the optimal amount. I set myself small goals – beating someone at playing pool, staying longer than 10 minutes at a party, and speaking to people who had been completely alienated by my behaviour when in the throes of my psychosis, were all things I had to achieve.

The word 'recovery' suggests getting back something you have lost or forgotten. I contest that after experiencing the earthquake in your life that is serious mental illness, your life is irretrievably changed. You will never be the person you were before. However, you may have more sensitivity, greater tolerance of others or deeper understanding of yourself – all of which can enhance your life and interactions greatly. Of course it is not easy, and time is the most effective ingredient. SMART goals that are Specific, Measurable, Achievable, Realistic and Timely, are useful as is having someone to confide in and who believes in you. I hated my parents for forcing me to deliver leaflets for a forthcoming local council election to the streets near their home, but in retrospect, doing *something* was massively helpful. Getting a sense of achievement and feeling part of something and being needed gave me a boost. I was lucky enough to be seen by a psychologist who taught me how to revise and who motivated me to learn and to work in mental health myself.

Recovery must be something you make your own for it to work. I used to work in 'vocational rehabilitation' (a term I find clumsy), helping people with mental health problems gain and sustain employment in NHS mental health services. Most of the people I supported were working in mental health services, as health care assistants, occupational therapy technicians and in administrative roles. A large number of the people I worked with had been unemployed for years and had often lost hope. However, the nature of the jobs I supported people into revealed a lot to me about the impact of experiencing enduring distress. People would often say that they would know they had put some significant distance between themselves and their 'illness' when they could use their experience to help other people. Of course it was not the case that anyone can tell others how to run their lives, or how they should behave to get well. Instead on a more subtle level, having been on a ward or in the depths of despair, old hands might understand the importance of being listened to and respected. Even working in office-based roles, knowledge of mental health services and being able to spell 'tardive dyskinesia' proves a vital and useful skill.

# How do you know when you have recovered?

Recovery is an elusive concept – as Perkins and Meddings (2002) suggest it is more important what an individual suffering distress states are their meaningful goals than for others to impose outcome measures upon them. NHS staff may state that compliance with medication indicates recovery, an individual may list being able to leave the house as a convincing sign. Already this poses a problem – with recovery and its indicators being conflated. Is recovery a stable state? a plateau someone reaches? Or is it when several signs are present or absent? By this I mean is recovery an internal state? Or is it a collection of external behaviours (or lack of them)? A person who is restful and calm may be deemed recovered if this is in contrast with their 'presentation' whilst 'unwell'. However, the absence of observable signs (perhaps their previous irritability and argumentativeness) of what is deemed illness may not in the service users' eyes warrant the label 'recovered'. Calmness may instead denote pessimism or withdrawal.

A further reason that 'recovery' is elusive is that, in my personal experience, even when you think you have reached the end of the 'recovery' road and you are as well as you can imagine, you can suddenly find yourself doing more, than you previously thought possible. I have wondered where the strength comes from; whether it is an artefact of 'surviving'. It is difficult to know whether, without an experience of mental ill health, you would be the person you develop into after such a massively life changing event. Some disabled persons are reported as stating that they would not change their disability. This is, perhaps, because people who have lived with disability have not had the experience of living life disability-free so would not know what they might be signing up to if they were offered it and enjoy themselves as things are.

Recovery, on the surface, seems to refer to the absence of psychiatric symptoms, though I believe it is possible for people whose symptoms are intractable to also experience healing and growth. There are situations in which 'dismantling' someone's belief system through therapy can be detrimental to their well-being. For example, someone who has understood they are a religious figure for years, without reprieve, may experience any acknowledgment that they have been mistaken as a serious personal injury. By this I mean that if there is no belief system to replace the longstanding and possibly socially isolating one, the individual may flounder. Instead of convincing someone their beliefs are inaccurate, recovery may involve discovering ways of their having conversations without referring to their identity as a religious figure and alienating others. By this I mean not referring to myself as God for example. Most people who have been around psychiatric hospital wards for any amount of time will recognise the feeling of realising you are talking to someone who holds ardent but in your view 'mistaken' beliefs. Recovery does not have to mean being like everybody else, but in my opinion it involves being able to gain from interpersonal interactions, whether they be verbal or behavioural.

## Realising the extent of the journey

When someone starts to get better, to recover, one of the first things to come to terms with is how far they have to go. Realising that virtually everything you have thought throughout an episode has been faulty is a difficult stage. For some it may seem easier to revert back to beliefs or a lifestyle that is familiar, if self-destructive. Remembering things you have done can cause more than the occasional shameful wince. Preaching to friends and strangers, arguing with people you care about on matters that no longer make sense (I remember being angry that I had been named Emma when getting to grips with my developing spirituality as it seemed a heretical play on the word 'Amen'), and countless other infractions of 'normal' social rules can make you not want to go out and face people ever again. It is in these circumstances that I find my sense of humour has been key. I have always enjoyed laughing and making others laugh, and I have managed to find a way of telling my story in ways that get some serious points across whilst using humour as a form of armour. Not that I believe in sugar-coating difficult experiences, but modelling a flexible and kind way of responding to and understanding your own life history helps others digest it.

## Employment

I have been described as someone who assumes they have the same rights as everybody else – and I agree I get indignant when others suggest I should be treated differently. I also believe that I have the same responsibilities as other people. I am obliged to work to keep myself in the manner to which I shall become accustomed (once I finally qualify and get paid as a professional rather than as a trainee, which is my current situation). I presented at a user-led conference in Oxford once and after expressing my views on the benefits of employment I was told by several of the attendees that work was irrelevant as it was hard enough to keep on getting your disability living allowance renewed and that having a mental health problem was a full-time job. Whilst I agree that distress takes up a lot of time and energy, I believe that if we, as service users want to be treated equally, we should **where it is conducive to good mental health** seek employment as should any other citizen. I add the caveat in bold as for some, employment is detrimental to their well-being, however much it is prized. Though working is a tonic, and feeling needed and supported is a boon to an individual's self-esteem (something that can take a long time to recover after each episode), trying to manage the pressures and muster the energies required as an intrinsic part of most jobs can be counterproductive.

Before developing psychosis, I was a student of social psychology in my first year at university. I am not quite sure why I chose psychology but now I do not know what else I could have done. I had no long-term plan about what I wanted to do career wise, but after scraping back into university to complete my degree I became more and more driven to work in mental health. It may sound trite but I found my experience of mental ill health gave me substance and my life meaning. I feel I have reached heights in my life I could not have dreamed of before. Of course as mentioned above I have no experience of the growth (or lack of it) I could have expected in my life without having schizophrenia. I am sure, however, that my experiences have rounded me as a person – both in mind through understanding what makes me tick but also unfortunately in body – through atypical antipsychotic medication.

## My identity as a psychologist

As mentioned above, I set great stall by taking something positive from my experiences. I have come to know myself and my likes and dislikes well, and have found that helping others is what makes me tick, though as I have said this is not entirely altruistic. Some authors, for example Young *et al* (2003) may argue that being driven to help others can be unhelpful in its extremes, subjugating your own needs for theirs. I believe there is a happy medium, I do not see helping others as altruistic; I gain rewards from such interactions. I enjoy making a difference, particularly in an area that is so beset by stigma. When in my vocational role, I once went to a party that was mainly populated by solicitors who responded by saying '*Oh how noble*' when I described my job. I do not feel I work in mental health for the 'kudos' or the sense of self-sacrifice but I would be lying if I said it was purely for other people.

After working in that job for six years I was accepted onto a clinical psychology doctoral training course. This was a massive boost to my ego and has provided personal development opportunities that I would have been hard-pressed to have found elsewhere. The training is, at the time of writing, coming to its end and I have four placements behind me in which I have worked with a variety of clients, those with severe and enduring mental health problems, people with learning disabilities, children and older adults. Though I have enjoyed working with each client group immensely and in different ways, I am now fairly sure I wish to specialise in working with people who have psychosis. Some psychodynamic theorists may argue that I am compelled to repeat my own experience with other people, or that my narcissistic traits are leading me to another messianic cause as a way of justifying this decision. Though this may be true, I like to think I am honour bound to help others navigate the difficult path that is recovery, having charted my personal map.

Working as a psychologist means I assume a variety of roles, assessor, supervisor, therapist, confidante, researcher, statistician and trouble-shooter. Each of these requires a differing amount of empathy, attention to detail and objectivity. I do not know how suited to stepping up to this plate I would have been had I not seen the 'dark side of the moon'. That is not to say that working as a psychologist or in the NHS is for everybody, or that you have to have personal experience to make a difference. For many, particularly those who have had less positive experiences of care, health settings are the last place they would want to go near let alone spend their entire working week. There are gains that surviving mental distress can offer, other than a sense of understanding a little bit about guiding others on the recovery journey. You learn what makes others tick, about communication, empathy, respect, giving people space and the value of individuality. These skills can be used in a myriad of ways to continue your and other people's development towards self-actualisation, or being the person you are destined to be.

## Stigma and disclosure

Recovery does not mean forgetting your experiences. I often bore others with the fascinating details of my fantastical inner thoughts – partly because not talking about them when they first started (because they scared me) meant I could not 'reality check' and they became still more detached from 'acceptable' thoughts. I have in my lifetime been very open about having mental health problems, even to random taxi drivers whom I am sure often felt fairly uncomfortable with my candour! My motivation to 'share' is propelled by the fascination and vanity I have surrounding having had such a dramatic, wonderful and terrifying experience. I have to remember that sometimes other people are not quite as interested as I am in the finer details of my delusional belief system. I have also long since learned that many of my thoughts were so idiosyncratic that I cannot adequately describe them to others, though they had a very powerful meaning for me. The flip side of sharing so much is having to deal with people stereotyping and being discriminatory.

Being a mental health vigilante and always jumping on any instance of general ignorance is sometimes counterproductive, however, and can perpetuate views of service users as over-sensitive and/or angry. Providing a calm model of thoughtfulness and fair-mindedness can, I believe, indirectly change more negative views than stamping your feet. Though it has taken me a long time to learn this, tuning yourself in to when it would be a good time to disclose can make a huge difference, in the middle of an argument or when the other person just wants to borrow a pen can make it an awkward experience. I tend to ask myself why would I be discussing the issue when I feel the urge to divulge my mental health problems. Good times are when I instinctively feel close to someone, relaxed and best of all when I think disclosure on my part may help them, myself or our relationship.

Reading *An Unquiet Mind* (Jamison, 1995) recently reminded me of the potential impact my mental health problems could have in the workplace, were I to suffer a (hopefully unlikely) relapse. In turn, this highlighted the importance of my feeling secure and supported enough to divulge the situation were this to arise. I am confident in saying that a team where user involvement is not just tolerated but celebrated will go a long way towards turning the inevitable disclosure into a learning space. I found the service I worked in prior to starting training epitomised involvement – acknowledging the unique skills, abilities and motivation of someone who has survived services and paying them to directly or indirectly help others find their way through this torturous maze.

I find using humour is a massive help though it can be a fine line to tread. I like making people laugh and I am aware that lots of things I have done have been very, very silly. However, I still resolutely want people to laugh with me rather than at me. I am in charge of what I tell people and I do not want others to feel I am 'vomiting information' for no real reason, as one of my friends puts it. The people I have most contact with – other trainee clinical psychologists and other people working in or being treated by mental health services, tend to be quite open-minded and positive about others' experiences of mental distress, so it is likely that I get a more informed reaction than most. Using humour can be a powerful way of explaining but also coming to terms with experiences that are difficult to process in any other way, though I have found that jokes about suicide attempts tend not to get a laugh. People who are not accustomed to talking about mental ill health issues either find it difficult to know when it is ok to laugh, or do not see the sense in discussing the topic because it is distasteful or frightening to talk about disturbed thoughts.

The reactions I have had from others range from the slightly too enthusiastic '*it must have been ace being God*' to the sensitive '*that sounds difficult – but it must help you at work now*' to the uninformed '*but God is a man*' and finally to the downright discriminatory '*so you are saying you are a nutter?*' To take a social model of disability view, obviously society needs to change (and reports such as that from the Social Exclusion Unit (ODPM, 2004) point out the exact ways this should happen) in order to understand, let alone accommodate people who suffer from mental distress. However, I like to feel I can take an active role in that process – from talking to the media, working as a clinical psychologist and writing this chapter. Providing a model of openness so others think it is ok to discuss unwanted thoughts and feelings will hopefully make mental ill health a 'water cooler' topic of conversation – one that is fine to have during the coffee break at work without feeling you are risking your friendships or your job. After all 'mental health' affects everybody (it is usually either sought or possessed) and mental ill health is something that most people will come into contact with one way or another over the course of a lifetime.

## Disclosure in the media

As referred to above, I opted to share my story of rebuilding my life in the media to generate awareness of what mental health and mental ill health actually mean. The general public is usually informed about the subject by titillating reports about homicide or ineptitude (though the former far outweighs the latter in coverage). People do not get to hear about the struggles people have to make every day to leave their home against the tide of bullying and insults. I found people were generally pleased I had spoken out once they got over the surprise of turning the TV on and seeing me there. A touching moment was someone I had never met coming up to me in the canteen at work, and after asking my name just saying 'thanks'. Another person left a chocolate bar for me in reception. I appeared on many programmes and never got mobbed or spat at in the street as I was concerned might happen. It was helpful to bear in mind that I was not going to be famous, particularly as believing I was God had made me sensitive to this and had rather put me off being in the spotlight.

I would really encourage as many people as possible to share their stories – there are so many of 'us' that we are the 'normal' ones and with enough people making noises we can only be accepted if not admired. It does take a certain amount of determination (and thick skin) to discuss highly painful experiences in public but the more people who do it, the more usual it will become. Hopefully in the future having a mental health problem will be seen in a similar way to being left-handed – only a barrier in terms of the tools society does not provide. Mental ill health could even be celebrated as a source of inspiration and as an expression of deep thought and sensitivity. This idealised state of interpersonal acceptance is a long way off, however, as other people tend to be hard to influence in the right direction.

## Relationships

As mentioned above, I do not feel that mental health and ill health exist in a vacuum that does not affect anybody else. I have spoken a lot about my own recovery in this chapter, largely because I feel it is such a personal journey that I only feel comfortable describing mine in depth (outside alluding to a minute part of the literature on recovery). A significant part of my experience has been developing a supportive life partnership. I do not know whether recovery enabled me to develop a solid relationship, or whether starting a personally meaningful and rewarding relationship helped me to feel I had recovered. In true chicken and egg style, I do not know which came first. However, not everybody needs a romantic relationship to prove or access their recovery. In fact, feeling comfortable with being alone for me was a major step in developing autonomy and moving away from being 'unwell'.

The idea that people around you have to recover too is taken up by some forms of therapy that address family issues – 'systemic' approaches to therapy suggest our relationships make us who we are, as such, any interactions we have affect us and our conversational partner. Though behaviours conducted mid-episode are out of our rational control, people actively having mental health problems are often very insightful about others' weak points or raw nerves. Trampling on these 'sore spots' though essentially often unintentional can make it difficult for others to trust or respect us even when the period of extreme mental ill health has passed.

## Spirituality and religion

An individual's relationship with others can be influenced by their spiritual beliefs, which in turn can help them understand their experiences. A cleric I once received therapy from described the experience of mental distress as '*walking alone in the valley of the shadow of death*'. For those who have taken this journey and survived the terror of being in the tunnel with no light visible at the end, it takes a huge amount of faith, in yourself or a greater good, to keep on going. Many authors such as, Fallott (2007) and Mulcahy (2007) have pointed to the value of faith in recovery. Personally, I was a committed atheist prior to experiencing psychosis, but found that my despair posed more questions about life, the universe and everything than it answered. There was a messianic component to my psychosis, perhaps leading me in the direction of religion (as suggested above I thought I was God), and I found the calm solidity of the church reassuring. Though many questions are raised by our own personal hell that we cannot easily answer, spirituality helps us frame these and offers an explanation of why they cannot presently be answered.

Mental health professionals sometimes state that expressing religious ideas may be an indication that a person is not 'well'. Religion and spirituality are, I believe, powerful forces that can act as a crutch for someone, and a way of meeting people, answering questions that seem impervious to other methods of enquiry, and allowing a sense of worthiness and lovability. As with any belief system, it is possible for ideas held rigidly by someone with metaphorical tunnel vision to become damaging to the individual and to those around them. I remember a friend I met at the day hospital I attended who believed that he was the Lamb of God, unfortunately this meant that he did not look after himself and died aged 34 through an act of 'misadventure'.

## Getting better: looking after yourself

I have attempted many methods of self-help, including complementary therapies – geared towards improving my mental and physical health. To date, these include giving up smoking, trying several diet clubs, full body massage, reflexology, Alexander technique lessons, chiropractor, colonic irrigation, Indian head massage, vitamin supplements, becoming vegetarian, taking courses in public speaking and getting exercise via the gym or DVD exercise programmes. These have had varying degrees of efficacy and some have been harder to maintain than others (especially exercise) but I feel strongly that I have to pamper and look after myself – very few other people will. Even if a therapy is not 'evidence-based', it makes a statement to myself and others that I am worth looking after and I do not have to just feel lonely or depressed. I can actively do something. Another area I enjoy delving into is cookery, having been encouraged at school and having parents who are both excellent cooks and big eaters. I often say it is the only creative thing I am any good at. It does, of course, have a down side – it is difficult to cook interesting food and not eat it, which can lead to a rapidly expanding waistline (especially at my age and on my medication). This has been offset somewhat by my recent interest in exercise, however (and I might even keep my fingers crossed I will keep it up this time).

I think it is important to find the things that relax you and to keep the materials you need for them together (be it aromatherapy oils or a diary in which you can confide) somewhere special, so you can select a remedy easily whenever you need to. Being (almost) a psychologist, I believe strongly that activity is a wonderful counter against low mood, even though I have to remind myself of this and force myself to start something when I am down. I recognise that it is not easy but neither is being paralysed by the dread and pessimism that is generated by endlessly trying to analyse a situation before attempting to intervene in it.

# Other therapeutic approaches

Recovery for me is very much about taking risks and putting myself in uncomfortable situations so I get to learn that both myself and others can cope with them, thus steeling you for future encounters. This is a premise for cognitive behavioural therapy (CBT), which I have tried and tested, having received it and provided it for others. Having seen it from both sides as it were, I feel that it can be a wonderful way of actively participating in your own recovery and feeling you have some control over it. Some people criticise CBT for implying that people are the authors of their own misfortune by 'thinking wrongly' – I prefer to frame it as a model where the solution might lie with the individual, even when the cause of the problem does not.

CBT does not fit the template of what many people view as therapy – there is no couch, you rarely lie down and there is usually very little reference to your mother's breasts. It requires energy and focus and often involves undertaking homework. The homework tends to be recording things like thoughts and feelings, or attempting experiments that you agree with your therapist. The therapist does not cast his or herself as the all knowing expert, but as an interested and informed ally who is interested in collaborating with you to find out what keeps your difficulties going and what relieves them. The partnership is very much like detective work, with both parties having different expertise in understanding the 'problem'.

# Maslow's hierarchy of needs

Maslow (1954) developed a model of the needs a person has to meet in order to survive and move towards the goal of 'self-actualising' (see **Figure 1**, p.96, Maslow's (1954) Hierarchy of Needs). This hierarchy is famously represented by a triangle with the more basic needs such as food and shelter at the bottom. I would contend that the process of 'ascending' to the level of self-actualising (realising your personal potential, self-fulfilment, seeking personal growth and having 'peak experiences') can be boosted by the self-knowledge that accompanies recovery – not only by the sense of achievement that results from overcoming your demons but from the grace that often results from having been faced with experiencing life at the bottom of the barrel, being at your lowest ebb and knowing there is nowhere further down to go.

# Young's schema approach

Young et al, (2003) developed an approach to therapy that aims to change patterns of behaviour that have been laid down since childhood and that govern our happiness as adults. They suggest that human beings need a particular set of experiences to develop into healthy adults. These include autonomy, secure attachments, (relationships with care givers) freedom to express needs, spontaneity and play and realistic limits. If any of these needs are not met appropriately, they hypothesise that problematic and deeply held beliefs about the self can result. Recovering from psychosis warrants using some of the techniques Young et al describe, such as empathic self-confrontation. This refers to being kind to yourself in understanding that certain patterns of behaviour were learned and helpful within the context they emerged from (empathy), but not allowing this to deflect yourself from the task of challenging and changing your assumptions and habits (self-confrontation). Though it is easy to blame others for causing us psychosis, even if in a myriad of ways the problem may have been theirs, the solution is often our own and may be learned and practised through personal experience.

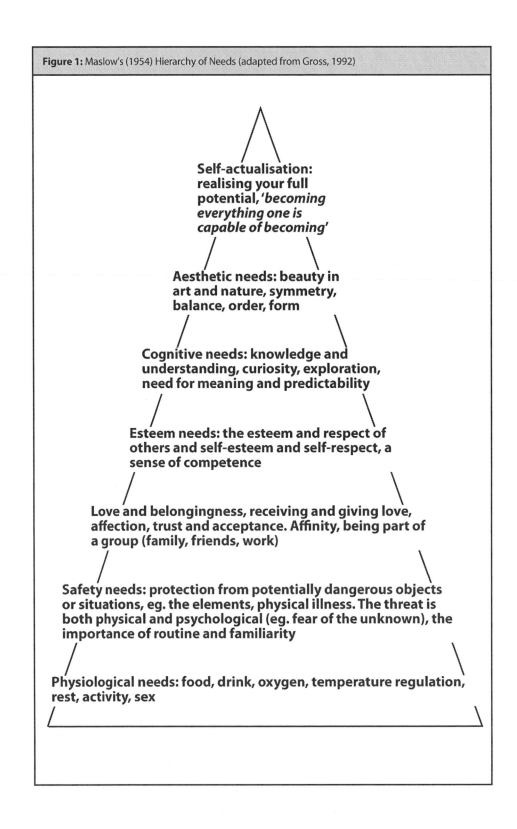

**Figure 1:** Maslow's (1954) Hierarchy of Needs (adapted from Gross, 1992)

**Self-actualisation: realising your full potential, *'becoming everything one is capable of becoming'***

**Aesthetic needs: beauty in art and nature, symmetry, balance, order, form**

**Cognitive needs: knowledge and understanding, curiosity, exploration, need for meaning and predictability**

**Esteem needs: the esteem and respect of others and self-esteem and self-respect, a sense of competence**

**Love and belongingness, receiving and giving love, affection, trust and acceptance. Affinity, being part of a group (family, friends, work)**

**Safety needs: protection from potentially dangerous objects or situations, eg. the elements, physical illness. The threat is both physical and psychological (eg. fear of the unknown), the importance of routine and familiarity**

**Physiological needs: food, drink, oxygen, temperature regulation, rest, activity, sex**

# How do you know recovery has worked?

I really do not know what 'recovery' is in any accurate sense, but that does not mean it is not something to strive towards. A tentative explanation might be that it is the elusive state of a degree of release or growth, often but not always pursued by individuals or their carers/involved professionals after experiencing mental distress. The areas I and my friends have considered when determining the extent of our 'recoveries' included:

- being free from voices or not distressed by them
- being able to leave the house
- having a job
- having friends and a social life
- being free from discrimination
- not needing to take medication (though I am still working on this one)
- keeping anxiety at bay
- maintaining positive relationships with friends and family
- being free from the danger of self-harming or suicide attempts
- not relying on alcohol or substances to mask or cope with pain
- feeling autonomous
- feeling loved, able to give love and deserving of love
- not standing out from the crowd on the bus or in the supermarket
- being able to pursue hobbies
- not being trapped in relentless self-destructive habits
- being free from distress

This is by no means an exhaustive list, many other things can be added but these areas are those I have experienced or observed in myself and my friends.

# Have I recovered?

As implied above, there is probably no true yardstick for measuring recovery however many questionnaires you fill out, simply because it is such a personal thing. You may feel you have never been better whilst mental health professionals remain concerned. Or you may feel embarrassed or stressed that there is still something evading you, another level to move up to when all around you are congratulating themselves on having done a good job in getting you well.

I chose to tell my story in the media; on TV and in the newspapers, so others might feel that it is ok to be proud of surviving mental health problems, not that they should pretend they were not there. I have met some familiar faces from breakfast television and magazine programmes but that does not mean my slate has been wiped clean and I am symptom free. I regularly experience the following:

- Paranoid thoughts: does this person I am talking to think I am odd?
- Intrusive thoughts: what would happen if I closed my eyes whilst I drove down this road?
- Voices: was that the radio?
- Confusion: what am I doing in the kitchen?
- Dealing with stress: I have to finish everything now or I will fail the course!
- Am I unusual? Do other people have these worrying thoughts all the time or is it just me?

The answer to the last question is 'yes' – most people will experience similar phenomena quite regularly, they just do not choose to talk about it. Having ongoing symptoms does 'not' mean you have not recovered or are not going to – it is how you cope with and manage the things they bring up, that is the key.

In conclusion, I believe everybody's recovery is their own, painful, intimate experience of self-discovery that can hopefully be transformed into a process of growth. It is not easy, never assured and certainly never complete. Despite this it can be the most vital and rewarding journey of self-discovery you can make. If you are on it, I wish you joy in your adventure.

## Some thoughts on good practice

So reading a book might describe what recovery is according to several survivors, but 'recovery' is a broad term, so how can it relate to an individual looking for some ideas? The following bullet points are designed to help readers make recovery their own.

For service users:

- Decide what you want to recover 'from' or 'to'. This may be a job, a hobby, a physical health concern, an interest, a 'symptom' or a friendship among other things.
- Decide how you would know you were there, who else would notice? What point would be an acceptable level of success?
- Break your goal down to SMART steps (see p.88). For example, if you want to run a marathon, the steps might include finding a running buddy, buying the necessary trainers, starting an exercise class, running one mile a day each week, then two, then three – you can build this up over time.
- Identify your resources – friends and abilities that will help you meet your goal.
- When problems emerge, think of as many solutions as possible and try the most likely, going back to the drawing board when you learn about what is or is not working – thinking flexibly about solutions is more powerful than any problem that can come out of the woodwork.
- Reward yourself for your successes and do not be too hard on yourself when things take a step back, there is always tomorrow and recovery means finding ways to get over setbacks too.
- You might be diverted into another goal – finding you enjoy yoga classes more than running may become a more important pastime, this is great – flexibility is really rewarding.

Your experiences may not fit easily to the examples given above so here is another:

- Decide to go back to work after a period of ill-health.
- Think about what you have enjoyed doing in the past – at work and as a hobby.
- Decide a career goal – eg. being a nurse.
- Find out what qualifications/experience are needed.
- Get some voluntary work to test it out.
- Decide a relapse/crisis plan with a mental health professional you trust.
- Identify your allies – people who will support you, and talk to them when things are difficult.
- Get a job as a nursing assistant to get experience and money for studies, talk about adjustments needed to help you do your job with your manager, such as time out for therapy appointments (these are called 'reasonable adjustments' and you are entitled to them).
- Do evening classes to get the qualifications needed for entry to nursing training.

- Find a course you can get to and apply, getting help from allies and people at work, reapplying after getting feedback until you get a place or find another more enticing interest.
- Enlist help from college support mechanisms such as disability officers and less formal avenues such as people on the course you get on with.
- Take time out when you need it.
- Find out about local NHS trusts that are positive about diversity and support people with mental health needs into employment.
- Enjoy your career.

This is not to say that this is an easy process – the last example could take years, but as long as you know your next step and you are aware of the resources available within you and from people and organisations around you, you are perhaps successfully 'recovering' – and I do not think there is any such thing as being 'recovered'.

For mental health workers:

Mental health professionals may be able to facilitate the processes and activities above. I always remind myself that if it was not for service users, people working in services would not be employed in the job that pays them. It is a job with many privileges – such as being trusted with the most difficult and painful thoughts and feelings people (who often start as complete strangers) can bear to disclose. This means the mental health professional has a huge responsibility – to contain, to bring comfort and support and to above all else, respect the humanity of people who have historically been rejected from society. To help manage this task, I try to keep the following in mind.

- Help individuals develop SMART goals (see p.88).
- Listen to service users' plans, hopes and complaints and state the help you can realistically give – and ensure you give that when it is expected.
- Explain why you cannot meet requests fully when unexpected circumstances arise rather than just ignoring promises.
- Work with the person, system, symptoms and diagnosis in that order of importance.
- Do not be afraid to gently challenge others when their practice is counterproductive – such as by asking 'how will that help Mr X?'
- Remain curious and mindful that even the most incomprehensible behaviour has a meaning and a purpose for the individual even if you do not understand their explanations/motives.
- Encourage individuals to write/paint/tell their stories to others to help them be processed and organised and so others can support them and be inspired.
- Reflect on your practice – what you did, why, what the consequences are (eg. what the other person might have understood from your actions and how that may make them feel) and consider whether you would do things the same next time. Other staff members may be interested in helping you to do this either formally or informally and you could perhaps ask a psychologist to facilitate a reflections group.
- Listen before you ask – a colleague once said to me that therapy has two sets of ears and one mouth; making your attentiveness and concern apparent can help build a strong relationship and enable an individual to develop their own solutions rather than always relying on other people's advice.

- Look after yourself and enjoy your job – it can be emotionally draining but it is hugely appreciated and particularly rewarding when you are feeling good about yourself.

## References

Descartes (1637) [online] available from: www.literature.org/authors/descartes-rene/reason-discourse.

Fallot RD (2007) Spirituality and religion in recovery: some current issues. *Psychiatric Rehabilitation Journal* **30** 261–270.

Jamison KR (1995) *An Unquiet Mind: A memoir of moods and madness*. New York: Random House.

Maslow A (1954) Hierarchy of Needs. In: RD Gross (1992) *Psychology: The science of mind and behaviour*. London: Hodder & Stoughton.

Mulcahy L (2007) My journey of spirituality and resilience. *Psychiatric Rehabilitation Journal* **30** 311–312.

Newnes C (2000) Can I see the test results please? *The Guardian* [online]. Available at: http://www.shropsych. org/testresultsplease.pdf (last accessed April 2009).

Office of the Deputy Prime Minister (2004) *Mental Health and Social Exclusion*. Wetherby: ODPM Publications.

Perkins RE & Meddings S (2002) What 'getting better' means to staff and users of a rehabilitation service: an exploratory study. *Journal of Mental Health* **11** 319–325.

Young JE, Klosko JS & Weishaar ME (2003) *Schema therapy: A practitioner's guide*. New York: Guildford Press.

## Chapter 10

# Re-covering recovery: dancing with difference in the hope of the yet to come

**Anonymous**

It is difficult to express my experiences of psychosis and recovery in a conventional linear narrative. To give some sense of how meaning in the present interacts with meaning in the past, I have reassembled pieces from different texts I have written over the years and which continue to matter to me[1]. One or two bits might be a bit challenging as, when lost for words, only critical mimesis saves me – by this I mean using a text or an idea as an echo chamber to try and say something different about it. I ask you to have patience with areas that might baffle or feel choppy and disruptive. They are included for two reasons. First, the uncertainty they point to were vital in transforming myself from someone with very little hope to someone with hope for recovery. Second, information coming in from different trajectories and in different styles was the closest written approximation I could find to convey the way meaning dances around, disconnecting and reconnecting with different parts of itself within experiences of psychosis.

## Bit parts

I have a memory: *'If you don't behave the policeman will take your name'*. With the literal imagination of the very young, this possibility was alarming. I was learning to read at the time and the power to attach words to things by no means seemed certain or secure. Would I be able to get my name back? How long would 'he' keep it for? What would it be like to have no name? How would anyone speak to a no-name? I rapidly drew the conclusion that I would become invisible and starve to death alone. As a direct consequence, I became very well behaved but nursed a small suspicion, nevertheless, that the policeman was remarkably similar to the bogeyman that lived at the end of the footpath by our house. Not long afterwards the dream started; a mistake on waking, which repeated itself with routine certainty for several months. Always the same thing, I would get up too early and go to the bathroom to brush my teeth. In the half-light, I would accidentally squeeze toothpaste on my father's razor and calmly, painlessly slice my gums away.

Later and not unconnected, I suppose, I recall pestering my father while he was shaving. It was one of those endless 'why' conversations that only small children and deconstructive philosophers seem to have the energy for. My father had some interest in science and was always keen to pass this on but patience had never been his strong point. I was on a roll that morning and had kept hold of his attention all the way to creation. '*If the universe began what was before the beginning? What's outside the universe and how can it have an outside if it hasn't got a proper beginning, why?*' – the non-origin of origin for four-year-olds for want of a better description. At last word point, dad decided there was 'nothing' outside, before or after the universe and I wondered if this was where the policeman lived.

It didn't make sense. On the one hand, how could he talk about nothing as if it were something? This would mean it wasn't a no-thing because how could a nothing be called anything and still not be a something? On the other, perhaps it could not be said at all without messing up the question. Possibly, and this seemed more appealing, there was a hidey hole in the sentence. I approached the issue cautiously and inquired why nothing had a name and, if so, could the policeman take it. Now he was going to be late and snapped that God and the policeman were one and the same and they were there to make sure that dads got to work on time. But children know when parents are just saying something to shut them up and I said so. My mother decided to lend some reinforcement to the proceedings. Something along the lines of, '*The lightning will get you if you speak to your father like that and if "God" doesn't do it, I'll rinse your mouth out with soap to prove it.*' Mother was a lapsed Catholic and children know how to slide into the blameless spaces between parental logic and not say so. The soap was disgusting but she had not rubbed my name off. It was clearly a con.

We had a large family table in the living room, or at least I remember it as large. I used to climb trees inside it, legs waving in and out like the joints of an impossible spider. Anyhow, I could still fit under it quite comfortably, lurking, like a troll under the bridge of meal times. The folds of cloth made a good hiding place but not as good as the hole in something. Still unsure about the policeman and the certainty of dinner, I wrote my name in big letters on my best doll, dressed her in my clothes and stuck her right in the middle of the room in case the lightning, of which I was only half sceptical, could hear. It was a good switch, she was I and I became invisible. Then I made 'her' say every filthy word I'd ever heard over and over again. I even grew bold enough to 'take' my name back and say them myself out loud. The fantasy of auto-genesis now complete, no lightning, ergo no policeman, ergo no one could take my name but I could write it 'on' things and displace myself at will! With lots of nothings, which always sounded like something, it was, I realised, quite possible to animate no-names for special purposes; a truthfully false hypothesis. It proved especially good at invisibility, not eating soap and exploring forbidden footpaths. As one would expect, the razor nightmare stopped, although the waking dream returned in adolescence in a mediated form.

Not long after this, our father threw the table at the wall. He didn't like eggs cooked that way. I remember trying out a new 'no-name', like a very thin glove, to squeeze through cracks in the anger. We made our escape to mother's studio and painted cheese bacteria, lots of them, which we had seen under his microscope; hundreds of beautiful aliens who were later to become our friends. We had many such adventures and, of course, we were sometimes caught out in the open. For these occasions, no-name would pretend to be an imaginary friend on whom all the blame could be placed. 'Nomie' aggravated everyone but was generally perceived to be an acceptable part of growing up. Her sidekick 'Ittle' (a contraction of it'll kill you, I think) was dutifully sanctimonious and aimed, generally, to convince every one that 'we' couldn't have done anything like that; a fake of a fake of a fake.... She wasn't very plausible and both departed before adolescence. No-name became a strong habit though and was very much in evidence all through teenage, her secret faded to forgetfulness by the time I gave birth to my son. She doesn't speak very much these days but always spots the things I miss. She is here now, weaving her imperceptible rhythms behind the back of my chair, her sharp white teeth making tiny bites round the words as they appear on the page.

We have said I many times and not said it once.

## Covering up hopelessly

The histories of madness have, until the 1960s largely been written by the winners – that is those with the power to write culturally relevant texts. To cut a long story very short, psychosis has stood outside the history of expertise and of appropriate knowing yet, until comparatively recently, has been contained inside institutions. Following Derrida's[2] lead, there has been meticulous analysis in the humanities of the relation between women as property and the philosophical 'quest' for the proper property of the real – writing in the margins of philosophy is, ironically, a standard motif of the postmodern. The material exclusions of women and other 'others' from these sites of cultural production are/were a good insurance policy for the Enlightenment ideal of 'man' as the measure of all things.

This idea of 'man', has little to do with actual men today. However, the idea of the 'same' man is deeply embedded in the way knowledge about psychosis has constructed 'the psychotic' as an 'object' as, by default, not as human as the knowing 'subject' of Enlightenment thought. Lived experiences of psychosis are homeless in these houses, off the rational calendar and thus a source of great fascination for deconstructive thinkers seeking to undo the double binds of Cartesian certainty. 'I think therefore I am' must forget its mad other as a condition of thinking at all. Hegel's desire for the absolute must cover the gaps in its logic, even Socrates[3] has to contend with the sophist. How does thought 'cover up' this most dreaded co-dependency? How is it possible to recover (re-cover from) traumatic events that (re) mark and have a repetitive force, which draw them like a tattoo across your brain?

These are difficult questions and ones that have taken years, more than one psychotic episode 'outside' the system and several academic disciplines 'within it' to get any kind of handle on. The tools I use to self-manage come from Western understandings of being a being in time, Hindu and Buddhist thought, Christian theology and not forgetting my very best dead enemy Frederick Nietzsche. The institution in which I was first admitted is next to the university I studied in – placing the 'losers' and the 'winners' in a close geographic relation. I live nearby but was studying history on a different campus (which was helpful). There was more than a little irony involved in studying the self-styled antichrist (Neitzche) in a theological college, but the struggle is what made the discipline to do it. I was experiencing what I thought were dead people under my tongue; it was a matter of some urgency to work out where they were coming from. Beliefs about the future interact with present and past meanings. The thought of the millennium was structuring the way different theories made sense of the past and, by default, the present. It doesn't take a lot of digging to see that the many understandings of change that historians use are secular variations on religious themes, but the more I dug the more all pervasive these seemed in psychological, sociological and political readings of history. The theories I liked best were steeped in contested readings of Nietzsche and Freud but none made much room for women readers.

As a postgraduate, I moved from history of ideas to cultural studies and performance art, using critical and creative tools to make a study of Nietzsche (read as my father), Eternal Return (1974) and the (alleged) non-existence of women in his texts (Oliver, 1995). This was a way of putting my past into a context that made sense to me at that time and a way of opening the ideas I liked to a different kind of reader response. If one is to study the structures of misogyny, one may as well study the clever ones. Practically, it was a good way of engaging with lots of debates without having to write too many words….

My first experience of being mentally 'unwell' started in my late 20s but looking back, I think I was 'unwell' in a different way before that. There were three phases over a long-time span covered with long intervals of 'well-being'. Each episode started off where the last one ended and each did a different kind of work. The first was coloured by extreme anxiety, the second by extreme anger. I don't have an appropriate word for the third, which was almost mystical but I think it was a working through of what was left unresolved in the first two. There are lots of reasons why I could have become 'unwell' initially. I could tick just about every box on the life events scale and was socially isolated, no family contact, poor housing, low income, hyperactive child and a recent head injury. My father also exhibits delusional symptoms – for example, believing his phone is bugged. A biological predisposition cannot be ruled out but at the moment my episodes are over 10 years old. So until demonstrated otherwise, the explanation that has the most meaning is a kind of delayed bereavement reaction amplified by life events and injuries.

My mother (Theresa-Anne) died when I was nearly 11. I was not there and the impact on me was not understood by my father or brother. This was not something I could explain to them. My mother and I had been very close and kept our conspiracies for good and bad. My father worked away in the week and my mother liked to paint and taught art. I liked to read books and, to bluntly put it, run amok in the country. We moved into a tiny village from the city when I was a baby and I have to say my mother was something of a cultural snob. I was not allowed to play with the kids on the council estate and there were no children my age in our street. I was not allowed to read Enid Blyton or Marvel Comics, the first was 'too mass produced' and the second was 'too American'. This didn't make me very popular but I did not mind that much. Books were much better than people and there were lots of animals around. I don't remember feeling isolated although I clearly was and I don't remember being scared of much – except for electricity pylons, piers, bridges with holes and escalators. These had the power to invoke terror. The pylons invaded my sleep as dreadful giants, surrounding the house. Piers and bridges were not so bad. They could be looked at and did not become objects of fear until they were walked on – it was all to do with seeing how far away the ground or sea was through the gaps. Escalators were of the same order as pylons and to be avoided at all costs.

With the wisdom of hindsight, Eternal Return was probably not the most sensible topic for a green and emotionally fragile undergraduate, but it is the choice I made (for good and bad) and has forced me to think about areas I most probably would not have thought about without the dilemmas it raises. The riddle is an existential test, designed to put pressure on the way people think about themselves. As here:

> The heaviest burden: what if a demon crept after you one day or night in your loneliest solitude and said to you, *'This life, as you live it now and have lived it, you will have to live it again and again, times without number; and there will be nothing new in it, but every pain and every joy and every thought and sigh and all the unspeakably small and great in your life must return to you, and everything in the same series and sequence – and in the same way this spider and this moonlight among the trees, and in this same way this moment and I myself. The eternal hourglass of existence will be turned again and again – and you with it, you dust of dust!'* – Would you not throw yourself down and curse the demon who thus spoke? Or have you experienced a tremendous moment in which you would have answered him *'You are a god and never did I hear anything more divine!'* If this thought gained power over you, it would as you are now transform and perhaps crush you; the question in all and everything; *'do you want this again and again, times without number?'* would lie as the heaviest burden on all your actions. Or how well disposed to yourself and towards life would you have to be to have no greater desire than for this eternal sanction and seal (Nietzsche,1974, p.273).

What if one day a demon were to creep after you? Nietzsche's deceptively simple statement of Eternal Return is, perhaps, the most cited and contested area of his thinking. Nietzsche asks us to select whether, if confronted with the proposal of endless repetition, there is not a single moment that would make the rest endurable or indeed divine. It is not for 'nothing' that Nietzsche, pedagogue par excellence, assigns the demon the dramatic privilege as the spokesperson for this task, or poeticizes the earthly yet aerial Zarathustra as rightful occupant of the cave in the heights. Nietzsche's (1974, p.181) proclamation that *'God is dead'* requires its own 'anti-parable' and this, understandably, is not good news for everybody. If, as Nietzsche contends, the 'soul' of the human is something made rather than given, then the 'demon' each reader imagines is the quickest way of resonating with all people at their deepest emotional levels.

**Dorothy started by saying dutifully (with Derrida) that reading(s) of Nietzsche had proceeded through a concern to establish the inviolability of his story forms, the story form of the question of being, the story of man's dwelling. She did not feel at home in the 'certain manner' of this story form, certain at the cost, it seemed, of the radical doubt that coloured most of her days. She was estranged within it and a stranger to it. But at no point did she see herself as the strangeness of it.**

There were two things I yearned for as a kid – a horse and a rocket. Most of my childhood years were spent in relentless pursuit of these two goals. The horse was the most attainable and tantalisingly close; there was a whole field of retired racehorses in the field behind our house and the hunt rode through regularly on the bridle track in between. My mother hated the hunt, saying it was the unspeakable pursuing the uneatable but all I could see was glamour and excitement. I had no understanding or empathy for the fox at that age and no sense of what capture would do to it. All I understood was that 'big girls' rode horses, wore smart red jackets and I aspired to be 'just like them'.

The horses were too big for me but I have always been tenacious. I am sure that having the freedom to try out riding the sow on a nearby farm would count as very bad mothering today. They can and do eat anything. My mother was very absorbed in her art when she did it and, as long as I did not call too much attention to what I was doing, I could get to do quite a lot unnoticed. I was about the same size as the piglets then so I got away with my first 'riding lesson' but it did stink, made loads of washing and you can only go so far with pig riding in a sty. I was swiftly banned from the pig farm. My mother investigated the source of the stench and rescued a dog en route – a Jack Russell/Corgi cross she had found tied up in a crate without water or food on the farm. There was a row and the RSPCA was called. We kept the dog and I was not allowed near the pigs (animal and human) again. TV had just entered our house and this was an amazing distraction. It ran on a slot meter so was rationed and something to look forward to. Lassie (sad but true!) was a very nervous creature and, at first, would only settle in the locked passage between the house and the garage (effectively a slightly bigger crate). So we put food and water in it and took it in turns to sit at a distance from her. Eventually she trusted and moved towards us. My mother already had a cat, Cocoa, a chocolate brown and extremely spoilt Burmese who plainly resented the newcomer on his patch. Lassie became my responsibility and while I felt faintly foolish calling her that at 15, she was a good friend and fellow traveller. As dogs go, she was quite smart and would take herself down to school at home time and wait outside the gate; but I still wanted a horse and, while Lassie looked as big as the TV wonder dog when she arrived, riding her was never really an option….

I (re) member the Equal Rights Act of the 70s. I (we still thought in these terms then) remember this day very well. I was seven and just stopped learning in imperial measurement (which is great for feudal exchange and rotten for place value, algebra and geometry). My mother, who was the youngest sister out of an extended London family, told me (I) was now equal to men. She was still quite healthy and (I) was chuffed but also curious. I had never understood myself as less than my brother. Although he was bigger, as all the extended family were, he was diagnosed with a learning difficulty quite early.

Re-cover that point – people didn't say 'learning difficulty' in the 1970s – my brother was backward, retarded, which was attributed to lack of oxygen at birth. (I) did not understand the change in the law – having never thought (I) was inferior anyway. My brother and (I) were very different. He could do things (I) could not and (I) could do things he could not. His pictures were exhibited in the Tate and (I) could only do tracing and not very well. He could not read much and I could read *The Telegraph* aloud at three. Admittedly, (I) didn't comprehend much but my mother put a lot of time into both of us, supplying me with books to stretch my imagination and developing my brother's art, which looked like it was set to become better than her own. We were awful to each other in private. For example, he ruined my toys so (I) cut his hair off. He was older and had more pocket money so (I) would make him pay to play with my dolls. We were allowed to run around on the beach without swimsuits because nobody thought about paedophiles as a threat in our village then. From the standpoint of (a) girl, (I) thought he was quite defective and 'fallen out' and, with his best interests at heart, told him '*to tuck it up his bottom*'. We felt awful about that, reading some of the histories of women's anatomy later on. We defended each other to the hilt outside. He was picked on by the other kids in the village and (I) got a few bloody noses sticking up for him. (I) re-member the day when he just put his head down and charged at one of the worst tormentors – just like the bull across the back of the way. (I) had experience of running from bulls but the tormentor was backed into a garage.

We were left alone after that.

The racehorses were mares and, at the end of their lives, out to pasture and tamer than the sow; the snag was still size. They were way taller than the pig but more approachable. I cultivated them assiduously, giving them loads of apples and carrots. Eventually, they would just trot up as I approached the fence. Learning the lessons of Lassie, the next stage of the operation was to climb the tree in the field and feed them from there. It worked and was quite easy from this spot to drop down on their backs and be carried around till I fell off (which invariably happened quite quickly). The field owner was not impressed and, once again, I was banned, and worst insult of all, given permission to ride the donkey. There was another horse, in a field by itself. I had been watching Westerns and just read *The Silver Brumby* by Elyne Mitchell (a romantic girly book about wild horses in Australia). I had not really grasped the difference between these fictional worlds and the world around me and was still smarting about the donkey. Caution went to the winds and I tried to lasso the stallion with my skipping rope.

Thwack!

All I succeeded in doing was hitting him around the ears with the handles. He (quite rightly) reared, jumped the fence and chased me down the bridle path snorting (unbridled) horse fury. I ran like hell and just made it to the plank bridge home before he caught up and reared again bringing its hooves down hard on the supporting beam. It twisted and I fell into a boggy ditch full of stingers … it was a hot day and I was only wearing knickers … when I came round, my body had more stings than skin. I had had most of the childhood illnesses by then, mumps, measles, chicken pox but nothing compared to this. I went into toxic shock and remember very little past hospital admission – I stuck to reading about gymkhana and the intricacies of dressage for ages after that – neat controlled horses whose rules of movement could be easily understood (and more importantly predicted). I entered the 'win a pony' competition but the dream in the now was gone. I had been watching the moon landings so my attention turned to building a rocket in the garage instead. Only the roof, I speculated, stood between my machine and the dream of space exploration in the very, very near future – not today – tomorrow maybe….

I grew out of horses, got into Star Trek and started reading sci-fi. Between us, my mother and I made sure the house was tidy on Friday….

**Eternal Return confronted me with the truly hellish proposal that eternal life would be, were it an achievable state of affairs. There would indeed be nothing new in it, nor, arguably, any means to individuate self from cosmos. If, for Luther,[4] the great papal swindle had been to make purgatory a marketplace, locating the origin of value outside this life would seem to be the 'indulgence' par excellence for Nietzsche. By constructing a mythical doer behind the deed of moral value, we are thereby 'saved' from the suffering of this world. Read as desire for the same, a 'tremendous moment' can at first glance replace the idea of God for the secular self. By providing an interior locus of value, other moments can be judged as good or bad according to how far they fit this one tremendous moment. This new human God may then generalise its highest point as a situated measure of all things. If no two moments can be considered identical, the result is lots of perspectives in which the moment ranked first by each person becomes a rule by which the rights of other moments are judged. While it is quite possible for a different 'tremendous moment' to elevate itself 'over' the rest in this perspective, there would thus always be 'one moment', or valuation, casting all the others into darkness. Those for whom suffering became dominant would be quite literally crushed by its own weight. Only those strong (or insensitive) enough to desire that their joy be eternal could plausibly survive this selective test [5].**

Life changed abruptly after my mother died and my father moved back home full-time. Up till then, I had had very little contact with him and had been very, very resentful of this. Why did my brother and I have to go out to play when he was home? The freedom we enjoyed during the week was not so enjoyable when it was forced upon us. It was soon realised then that my mother had kept us out of sight for a reason. It is still a source of great sadness that he could not come to terms with having a son on the autistic spectrum and an academic daughter. He believes and continues to believe that all women are biologically inferior and effectively 'the same'. We wondered for many years how my father dealt with the cognitive dissonance. I had spent the last two years of primary school helping the other kids with their reading and doing 'special projects' as I was too young to go to secondary school. My father's answer usually turned on something like enough exercise and discipline would bring my brother up to speed (he had been in the RAF). He himself had been a late developer and this was just how it was. Girls, on the other hand, were too unstable to concentrate on serious work. I just ignored this to start with and did my own thing out of sight. I wanted his approval and did anything to get it.

**Dorothy felt the wind picking up. The absolute strangeness of Eternal Return subordinated to this story form; itself subordinated to the story form of 'his' metaphysics had already spooked Toto, ears flattened to his head. It was approaching noon. The little prairie house did not feel at all inviolable, shutters clacking and pots rattling. The elders were out so she looked up the insurance policy**

just in case. It had distinct limits. Eternal Return, Dorothy read, provides *'both the metaphysical ground of being and the non-essence that conditions it'*. Eternal Return emerges *'solely within the scope of that interrogation that has put beingness into question with view to its projective realm and grounding of that realm'* (Heidegger, 1982). For such an interrogation to occur *'the guiding projection of metaphysics and thus metaphysics itself have already been thoroughly overcome, they are no longer admitted as constituting the primary and solely definitive realm'* (Deleuze, 2006).

What my father really loved was singing and opera. Not just any opera. He appeared at Wembley more than once. I loved accompanying although, sadly, not very tunefully. Being on stage was a family tradition. His father had been part of a radical Marxist theatre company and my father had started work doing the lighting, moving on to train as an engineer and then into more technically specific work in refrigeration. His voice was powerful and classically trained, projecting emotion into a bass baritone that could fill a room. I like Pagliacci now but hated it then. Some of the best (re) memories of my father are bound up with those rehearsals. He looked like Topol and was cast as Tevye in Fiddler on the Roof – 'Tradition', 'Sunrise', 'Sunset', 'If I Were a Rich Man'....

Equal to what?

There was only one actor on the household stage. My father's mother and sister supported but did not in any way challenge his 'authority'. He got a new and important job, designing test chambers for missiles and rockets. I was impressed but my mother's family stopped visiting us about then. Looking back, I can see why relations may have cooled with active protesters for nuclear disarmament but it was hard on my brother and I. A lot fell on my shoulders, cooking, cleaning shopping and I wasn't especially good at it. The house became dirty and we smelt bad. I hadn't resented looking after my mother when she was ill and while I did a lot of the physical work, she retained responsibility for letting me know when the washing needed doing and what buttons to press. I resented being shouted at to do things without any explanations about how and started misbehaving, truanting from school and running away from home to go to parties with my friends. Having dirty clothes was ok if you were a punk and, for once, I felt like I fitted in. God Save the Queen! The punks I hung around with got into loads of trouble and you could call them criminal but it was never for material gain. It was all about making an anti-establishment statement – for example, stealing a burglar alarm or breaking into the brewery to return the empties. I became an accomplished liar to make a space where I had some friends. My brother started setting fires and putting them out so he could look like a hero. I was sent to see a child psychiatrist who took a dim a view of The Sex Pistols, as they did. My brother simply shut down....

**Who me?**
**There is no witness**
**The true art of lying is to fake it,**
**– deny that you have faked it and then deny that you have denied it**
**– a perfect crime**

My father just did not know what to do with a daughter he could not control and the change in me disturbed my brother. I was physically assaulted many times in that house. I have no wish to describe this time as it has been let go already. Nevertheless, one event remains fundamental to my personhood today and that was being gagged and tied to a chair to make sure I did not run away. The only way of getting through this time was a) to pretend not to be there, or b) to focus on undoing the knots imaginatively. Things came to a head after a holiday abroad. My brother developed peritonitis in Italy and my father hadn't got insurance. He had to stay behind to sort things out and I went home. He gave me five pounds and was gone for two months. I got a job and ran up an enormous milk bill. I thought I had done quite well considering. My father didn't see it that way but this time I knew I could live on my own. I left school soon after that. One doesn't have to be a therapist to work out that I was angry at my mother for leaving me and was taking it out big time. I wasn't old enough to think this through at the time and nobody raised it with me – not even the child psychiatrist. It was only on handing myself in to the police and the subsequent court case that my teachers came forward and testified to their 'concerns' for me at school.

**Dorothy could feel the walls starting to vibrate. There did not appear to be an underwriter and, even worse, the policy did not seem to have ever admitted of girls. The margin for miscellaneous objects, goods and chattels might be one avenue of approach. She dismissed the option after a few seconds. At best guess, analysis interminable over the small print would keep the lawyers greased for years and she would still be unlikely to file a suit for damages.**

It is with deep remorse that I look back on leaving my brother in that house. When I went back 10 years later, there was nothing left of the artistic boy – only the bull remained. Care was not very good care so I absconded quickly, living anywhere that was dry and quite often already containing a furry population! This was not as bad as it sounds. People react violently to rats and other so called 'vermin' but they are just hungry animals. I was hungry myself so it made sense to feed them as well. I was never bitten and have a lot of admiration for what rats can do – for example, making themselves flat to squeeze through tiny gaps. They are quite intelligent and not aggressive if you don't give them meat – we co-existed well enough. Having established a safe sleeping place, I worked up to a lovely mobile home when my son was born but it involved fetching water and had no mains electricity. We both contracted pneumonia and I was grateful for the offer of social housing when it arrived. My new neighbours were not so impressed and raised a petition against 'pikeys' moving into the street. It was a fishing village where everyone knew every one else and, apparently, you didn't count as a local until you were third generation. I ignored them and they ignored me and I eventually made friends with some of the other mothers I met at nursery. It is fair to say that I overcompensated in being a mother and was over protective. My son suffered from febrile convulsions and I didn't like leaving him with anyone that would not know what to do. However, I needed to work and that involved hiring a child minder. I was studying for university and had nearly finished my A levels. I coped as I had always coped until he was involved in an accident while I was away. Not that big as an event in itself but it seemed to domino through every other life event.

The nails in the floor joists were out of joint, tiny mannequins spinning erratically and then appearing to jump, like lemmings, into the hollows opening in their absence. Dorothy thought she should try and secure the animals in the yard, at least, but it was even more inhospitable outside. The neat straw bales, only recently gathered, had detached themselves from their stake in the earth. Hay scattering all over, dotted with crows, also fleeing the enclosure. A few had been sucked into yellow arrows, thick as sticks and sharp enough looking. The roaring wind had the upper hand, for the time being. Dorothy caught a glimpse of Betsy, her treasured rag doll, snagged on the weather vane, whirling to a continuous blur of pink. She and Toto were not floppy enough to go round quite so fast. Her family might have to write the home farm off, if they made it back in time. She clicked her heels together nervously, fervently wishing for wings. She did not want to think about 'if not', about 'having nothing' and going 'someplace else' all alone. Her ankles started to bleed, staining her slippers. For now, she and Toto were safest in the eye of the cyclone, a relatively calm depression. Best to try and stay put....

The ground just opened up, alternating between extreme anxiety where I was going to die in my sleep and disassociation from everything around me. Obviously, it was my mother that had died in my sleep but I wasn't in a position to reason this out. It was more like a compelled acting out. I started making myself complan and eating rice pudding, which was how I had nursed her towards the end. I couldn't sleep at all and this went on for over a week. The lack of sleep was a rift in time. The longer it went on the more intense the experience became. The washing machine caught fire and I became hysterical. I started having panic attacks that felt just like having a heart attack and I became ultra sensitive to everything. Sometimes, my mind was going faster than I could speak so everything that came out hardly made any sense. Other times, I just couldn't get any thoughts together at all. I was in no state to look after my son – the crunch came when he threw up over me in front of the GP. I recall howling and rocking back and forth. I was advised to go into acute care as a voluntary admission 'just for a few days'.

Apart from the dying in my sleep there was no serious delusional stuff. I'm not sure I was psychotic in the beginning. I think I was in cumulative shock with it all and that short-term tranquilisers and some follow-up counselling would have worked then. However, I have definitely experienced psychosis since so I can't be sure. The anxiety levels went through the roof in hospital. A few days turned into weeks then months. I was put on antipsychotics straight away and the dose went up and up. I started drinking mineral water by the bottle to clear the effects and, when I could, hide the pills in a tooth cavity. I became convinced that the psychiatrists were sorcerers making minions out of the clients and that they were being used as a communications device to influence world events.

Reflecting back, it is not hard to see where these delusions came from. There was a social reality to the fantasy insofar as it explained the way power worked in the hospital. I'd been very active in CB radio and militant in the campaign to legalise it on AM so this was the practical experiential source for the communications fantasy. However, something else was going on too. I now understand from research in performing arts that affects travel in groups in ways that are hard to explain. Affects are contagious! What I was witnessing but did not understand is how transference of affect can be manipulated. I didn't have the frames of reference to express this at the time, or confidence in my hearing (which was already quite tuned in) to say I 'know' you are not listening, that all you hear is what you already know and that this is narrow-minded, objectifying and as full of prejudice about single parents in social housing as my neighbours with the petition. I was 'known' instead through tick-boxes, categories in which I was already doomed to a life of relatively low achievement compared to the skills I had. *'If she makes a full recovery she might make it back to being a care assistant'*. There is nothing wrong with being a care assistant but there is a lot wrong with having all your aspirations disregarded.

Some members of staff found it funny to wind the clients up. I remember being told that I had to keep the transmitter secret but she knew someone I could talk to at a later date. This was both a cruel and dangerous use of power and it had disastrous effect. I had been talking a little when I came in but stopped altogether when I 'knew' there was a witness to my 'truth'. I was treated with quite a high dosage of antipsychotics that started at home. There were a lot of physical side effects, which, at the time, I thought were part of the illness. The inability to settle anywhere was the most debilitating. If I went outside, I would become anxious about being outside. If I went in I would become anxious about being inside. Most of my time was spent walking backwards and forwards between these relentless extremities. I know every crack in the pavement on the green....

Apart from the newly acquired learning, all I really had were the books of my childhood, in which the eponymous girl hero was often capable of strange or magical things. I noticed very quickly that if I coughed down one end of the ward, it would take about 10 minutes to reach the other and started trying this out with more concrete gestures. For example, walking with my arms crossed – it took about a week for everyone else to start doing that. I started to get quite excited about this but some awful things were happening as well. Each psychiatrist that saw me went off sick immediately after meeting me, in quite extreme ways, broken arm, heart attack, etc. The evidence of experience fuelled a belief that the sorcerers had no power to touch me and that harm came to those who tried; and the delusion stuck to moral genre. If I used my power to harm for self-serving ends, the sorcerers would claim possession of my soul.

Delusions have a life of their own and want to survive at all costs. Becoming untouchable made it possible to believe the fiction without any further concrete evidence. I was never sectioned but it was made clear that if I tried to leave I would be. I wanted to see my son but it was decided that this was not 'appropriate' but nobody told me who was looking after him. I believed that he was being held hostage against my good behaviour, which in a way he was. I needed to find him but also refused to collude with what I understood as demonic forces. The way out was to pack my head up and send it 'elsewhere' while the rest of me figured a practical escape. I had done some meditation along these lines before I went into hospital and, in true ostrich style, figured that if I didn't know where most of me was they wouldn't be able to see me either. I would be safe and no one would get hurt. It worked but perhaps too well. I still believed that I would die in my sleep so I was not going to go voluntarily, but I was becoming exhausted by staying awake and resisting the medication. The fear levels around going to bed intensified. When I did doze off, I would be woken up for sleeping tablets. In my view, those that were supposed to be helping me were trying to hasten my end. Concentrating on not being there was probably what got me through at the time – a kind of self hypnosis; a way of going under without going under. Initially, I refused to speak as I saw this as collusion, but as the meds went up, won't speak turned into can't speak ... not I/not here/not anywhere in particular....

The gag was back on with a vengeance but I remained intermittently aware of myself at a distance. I wrote to staff but nobody responded; they did not check my records and contacted my father. After a while, the empirical evidence of having woken up each morning kicked in and the anxiety started to decrease. I was not compliant with treatment but the CPN only came round once a fortnight so it was possible to fake to his expectations. I had several bad fits as the medication wore off.

All in all, Eternal Return of the Same[6] (Klossowski, 1997) was turning out to be a bit of a nightmare for Dorothy. Even though there were moments that made the rest worthwhile in the terms of an individual life, affirming this also meant affirming all the suffering in the world that had led up to it as 'justified' for that one moment to occur. One would indeed have to be well disposed towards oneself to affirm all the suffering in human history and for me, it also meant never getting out of that chair. I thought of my father's history as a London boy, evacuated to the country in the war and how this had come to a head between us. He is set in his ways and my brother was lost and I did not love myself enough to want the same for my son.

But I hoped that things could be different...

# Starting in the middle

Derrida liked dancing with the pen and was very good at it.

We like starting in the middle

Like this

In the histories of madness,
Experiences of psychosis have no figure.
There is 'nothing' outside the text
But we have been regarded
As 'no-thing'
Outside/inside social texts

An object
Sat
In review
Surrounded by experts

Tied up in knots

And speechless

?

We like having a (body)
But it is not (a) property of exchange.

It is our territory and (well) guarded 'anti-body'

Living in hesitation-suspense
And cold mimesis-

Sat
By the freezer
Unravelling knots

And tying more
To cover us

# Re-covering hopefully

What if joy has no greater joy than in its own transitory nature? Stressing 'this same way' to breaking point, Eternal Return also puts pressure on the structure of repetition that supports the idea of one moment to which others may lay claim or strategically 'fail' to do so. Once the absurdity of life outside life is 'revealed', repetition no longer bears on a first time which escapes it, the tremendous moment is already engaged in a process of active forgetting, *'all joy must say fade go'* [7] (Nietzschze, 1969). It is no longer a question of thinking in terms of something that repeats identically over time. Rather, it is more useful to think in terms of repetition repeating itself differently. In this view, the riddle will, by definition, escape Nietzsche's presentation of it. The desire for eternity that pertains to the 'same' narcissistic ego must find ways to affirm its own impermanence and, paradoxically, to love it.

This made more room. In this logic, we were no longer the mad 'others' of a myth we had never bought into. We still had the problem of yearning for a speaking position. The texts and people we met at university construct femininity as a lack at the heart of being, driving masculine desire to have this impossible object. Taking up a speaking position in this economy perpetuates this lack, positioning psychosis as a failure to take up a viable position in an economy that already erased us. Putting it bluntly, it is not the best career move to admit to any kind of fragility on the lecture circuit....

Glimmers of (re)covery came from outside the statutory sector. I paid for my own counselling, which was very effective but probably not in the way it was supposed to be. I couldn't quite bring myself to self-disclose in the sessions but watching her watching me gave me a sense of being there that had been missing for a long time. I mimicked her reflections and, as this went on, the roles reversed and she broke down and told me her life story! The counselling ended when she said she didn't need me anymore. It is fortunate that I have a sense of humour because once again my attempts to get help ended up with me being the supporter. Nevertheless, I gained some important tools that I have gone on to refine. My social worker was also very good but again not in the way she was supposed to be. As long as my son was provided for, she did not draw attention to my times 'out' at home. She recognised the level of distress that the thought of hospital invoked and my existential right to do as much as I could for myself. The family aide was the best practical support. It took a long time to bond with my son again and she stuck with that process, playing with my son at the park when I didn't have the energy to do it. Both were non-judgmental and honest – saying what their working remits were and giving me space to sort myself out.

The most hope came from the educational sector and from friends. My social net evaporated during hospital but two stuck by me. One met me down the shops shortly after I came out of hospital, looking like a rabbit in the headlights. She invited me round for coffee and accepted my speechlessness and said I could come round every day and just sit there. This gave me a reason to get up and became the beginning of a structure. I did an adult return to education class when I was still shaking off the meds. I just couldn't seem to get the sense of words even though I knew that I knew what they meant. It was like someone else knew them. I went on to do an access course with the same tutor and was more awake by this point. However, I tried to jack in the course on the final assignment. She told me straight that I feared success more than failure and that she believed that I could achieve and would not accept the resignation. She was sticking her neck out in the hope that I would come through, but I had also dropped out of three A levels before becoming ill and the tutor knew this. It was quite a risk. I did pass and we are now close friends.

My access tutor was exemplary of what a hopeful attitude can achieve and I am beginning to see more of it in mental health services. My extended family were very kind. The contact with my father was, however, doomed before it began. He had developed controversial views about the way the universe works and had lost his job over them. He had even gone so far as to pin his alternative theses (après Luther) on the cathedral door. The punk in me quite liked this about him. What I didn't like was his unwillingness to examine his beliefs. He would simply say that good science would win out and then cite Galileo. To make a living, he had bought a shop and employed my brother as shelf-filler but he regularly chased the customers out for ruining his display! Again, I could admire my father for making a workplace for my brother, even though it was a shock to see how locked in he had become. I worked there for quite a while and could not reach him at all. My father was still as controlling and, I think, he actually quite liked it when I was docile and medicated. It vindicated him. Neither he nor my brother could grasp that I would be different 10 years later and the one thing that could not be mentioned was my reason for leaving in the first place. When I really started getting better he would insist I was becoming ill. He kept telling my son I was going to die, which made him very anxious. I did not understand, as I do now, that my father was most likely on the autism spectrum too and could not handle the variation in others or discern much difference between myself and my mother. One day, I just had enough. He had barged into my house when I needed to be quiet. I politely asked him to leave and he wouldn't. He told me to make him leave so I hit him over the head with a saucepan and called the police. I didn't hit him in an unrestrained way but all kinds of physical violence are upsetting reminders/remainders....

The second episode took the form of oscillating between thinking I was a spaceship and a fly. I needed a way of explaining to myself where I had been under the evacuating effects of the meds and the forgetfulness that followed. I was also furious and shocked at my own action and these emotions just kept escalating through hot rage to what I can only describe as cold malice. I think I could have become quite dangerous at this time but I stayed indoors and rode it out – the spaceship was a way of being above it all so that I would not actually hurt anyone (despite my very developed weapons system!); a means of being invisible (cloaking device) and a stealth operation (for navigating people when I had to leave the house). The fly gave a way of engaging with the world where what is usually imperceptible is perceptible. I was being overwhelmed with sensory input and needed to filter it in some way. Being a fly was a way of navigating my very short attention span when I was not a spaceship and made it okay to walk round in circles quite a lot! It was probably healthy to express some of the anger I had bottled up over the years but there was also a sense in which it was too much for me – I didn't have the words or actions to fit it. I have been treated in inhuman ways so it makes sense that I should experience myself as inhuman for a while. Within the terms of the delusion, I had to get the spaceship to land back on my head or I would crash while the fly experienced the world through openings in the feet. There were also times in which I thought I was the Angel of Death and a visitor from another planet.

**Dorothy stared at the flat legs of (a) woman, protruding out from under the strange place in/ on to which the little prairie house had landed, perfectly intact. She did not look too much**

to worry about, with stripy socks and all. Perhaps she was exotic. The dead woman had been in possession of a particularly fine pair of red court shoes, encrusted with rubies. She slipped them on. They felt as if they had been made for her. Dorothy heard a rustling in the undergrowth. Dwarf like children, first hesitant and then jubilant at the demise of the witch, danced joyfully around the little prairie house, calling Dorothy to join them. They lit a fire and hung a large cooking pot over it. The witch was dead; an event that called for a feast. Dorothy could not help noticing that they all looked very much the same, an un-individuated 'they' that seemed to do nothing but eat, laugh and eat some more. She wondered if they would eat her if they became terribly hungry or exchange her for more meat. They were singing about a yellow road to the greenest of all places and were suggesting that she and Toto follow it there.

Obviously, I am not a spaceship or a fly – they are figurations of transcendence and immanence, useful fictions populating the holes in reason, replacing its concept fetishism with images to move around with and to create a sense of skin in the world. I 'flew' around my daily life for months getting the fit right and bringing my anger down to a safe level and I still rely on my feet to feel what is going on in a situation. Apart from the saucepan, I believe that my mind would rather produce this kind of fantasy than vent its spleen on another person. So maybe the fairy tale made good at that point. During this time, another close friend managed my finances and made sure I had food. I was not actually eating any of the food she brought as I thought I could live on honey and water (which I did for several months). At the time, however, all I knew was if I let anyone in I would be sectioned for sure. My friend agreed to keep her distance only if I opened my curtains each morning to tell her I was okay and that she would call the emergency services if I didn't open them. I kept this arrangement, even in the worst parts of the experience. This gave me the space I needed to work things through and gave my friend enough reassurance to keep on. The most important thing in this experience was being able to trust someone within the chaos. This was a turning point because, from here, I began to hope that trust in other people might be possible….

It all sounded benign enough but there was a catch – a tin man that needed a brain, a straw man that needed a heart and a lion that needed some affects, bravery being the most urgent. They would join her en route. Dorothy was suspicious. She already knew that the guiding project of metaphysics had been looking for those renegades for years and had not managed to track them down. Only faith in their eventual capture could appear to promise to make good all three in the event of the kind of crisis she was now in. She cautiously asked the party where their father was. They shuffled uncomfortably, and backed round the cooking pot. Then, in unison, they sang of a wizard that lived in the greenest of cities, the Emerald City, the most immortal of cities. Only he had the power to return her to Kansas City safe and sound and only he could give out real brains, hearts and affects. It sounded like a trap, or hot air, or both. Worst case, she would be forced into skipping that road ad infinitum, speeding up the digestion of innumerable Christmas dinners or slowing them down, depending on one's point of view. This, she mused, was going absolutely nowhere and couldn't even turn up. Dorothy cast her mind back to the last glimpse of Betsy. Best guess, she had already done for one point on the weathervane, now spinning awry. Perhaps, there was an opening that Dorothy might also fit through? The red shoes were starting to rub her ankles so she slipped them into the pot unnoticed. They would break down soon enough, although the stones might not be so easy to digest – unless they were paste. She edged out of the foliage around the clearing, sliding incognito though the plans and projects that the party had designed for her.

The third episode was much more complicated. The first two involved an uncritical belief in the fantasies. This time, I was half way through a history degree (mainly history of ideas) and waking up a dormant learning spark. It was not acceptable, from my research base to fill in the lack at the bottom of historical understandings of cause with myself or the fictions I inhabited. This was Nietzsche's big mistake at the end of his writing life. I also live near a graveyard. This time, the spaceship had crashed deep underground in the graveyard and I had to get home to myself by walking through it. I'm an atheist but at this time, I really believed that the dead were bubbling up under my tongue and, at times, physically experienced being invaded through the flesh by them. So much for being the Angel of Death! The fly delusion was back but this time it was not safe to put my feet on the ground as this was how the dead came in – I jumped around the house quite a bit working this one out....

My brother was jealous of my son and stuck his fingers in the light socket. This also went into the delusion. I next believed the floor was being electrified through the internet, which I did not have but I believed had escaped the phone lines around me. Fine in spaceship mode as a source of energy but in fly mode the only way to move around was to stand on things that, in my mind, broke the flow of the electricity and hid me from the internet. This was terrifying but not as horrifying as dead people coming up through my feet, so it had a bizarre functionality in solving the problem of standing up. The house became littered with objects that would allow me to walk around (when I wasn't holed up in bed too frightened to get up at all). I have since discovered that my house had an electrical fault and was actually dangerous. Moreover, all the objects on the floor followed the actual wiring of the house of which I had no knowledge. So there were elements of fact and necessity within these delusions.

My human moods were returning but, oscillating between intense joy and intense horror, felt too big for my body. I needed to experience them in and 'outside' my body for a while before I could absorb them. The openings in my feet remained the interface between the earth of the graveyard and my body, so I learned how to withdraw deep into my body and hide in my spine while breathing them out or, again, I would be possessed. This escalated from all the dead people that could possibly be in the graveyard to my family and then philosophers I had read. I do not have words for how frightening this was but the philosophers weren't as frightening as the rest and I made 'friends' with them. I was very tempted by the thought of some very good essays but this would be plagiarism and would lead to possession of my pen! So once again, the decision was about using special powers for self-serving interests. But by not using them, I could not disprove them.

This time one of my footnotes came through under my tongue and I realised that I had written it quite recently. From this point, it was possible to see what was going on although there was no simple process to stop it. I had done well at university and gained a lot of self-worth from good marks for essays so lots of incentives to build on this. The first rule of historical thinking is learning to select and to account for that selection (the past is after all a very big place). By breathing out the voices, it was possible to listen to them (and talk back); decide which ones to keep and what to do with the rest. I would sit with my hands in the freezer to draw a line between human cold and dead cold in my imagination. I, literally, copied the cat and learned how to sleep with one eye open and switch off different bits of my body and brain at different times so it all rested. The spatial syntax shifted around. Sometimes, I was the spaceship or the fly – sometimes I was a fly and/or alien visitor in the spaceship. I named myself 'the girl in the middle' of all these fantasy projections. The way I decided between the honest and deceitful voices was to write my signature at the same time as breathing them out. This had little to do with authorisation and a lot to do with consent. If I felt my hand being pulled in any way, it was not allowed but had to be dealt with – for example learning to act rather than lie. Gradually the voices under my tongue crystallized as older and younger selves; warm memories of being mothered and mothering became a system of internal self nurturing between the older and younger bits, drawing them into a coherent 'whole' but, and this distinction is crucial, the 'whole' could only be maintained by drawing a strict line between us and the outside world, which was more than us. This process was all consuming, an intensive 'extra-spection' in which my mind congealed into shapes I could live with.

I have not had another episode since doing this work.

# Dancing with difference in the hope of the yet to come

**We cannot recover childhood innocence**
**Nostalgia for 'before'–**
**Projected onto 'tomorrow' in which we emerge perpetually untouched and unscathed**
**From a filthy ditch –       – covered in rashes**

There are two distinct ways of readings of the world, summed up in the two formulae *'only that which resembles differs'* and *'only differences can resemble each other'*. The first *'invites us to think about difference from the standpoint of a previous similitude or identity; the second invites us to think similitude and even identity as the product of a deep disparity'* (Deleuze, 1994). Both ask thought to open to the uncertainty at the heart of thinking about thinking. Eternal Return of the Same allows us to think of recovery as a former state of innocence to be recuperated or end state to be attained. Yet it also involves the repetition of a story form that erases us – a rag doll tied to a chair separated from what we can do. The repressed force of this story form constructs us as dead before we have lived; a mad 'other' travelling with the ones we have lost; playing havoc under our tongue. This narrative still has the force of a black hole, sucking us in to the closed repetition of hopelessness and negative stereotyping that is attached to experiences of psychosis. My son had a hard time growing up through all of that. He was in care several times and didn't understand what was going on. He has the coping strategies of an old man and I wish he could have had longer without learning them.

Only thinking from the latter perspective can 'ground' the idea of recovery as re-covering. What I mean by this is repeating traumatic events differently within a world whose fullness and openness both eludes and informs them. Freeing thought from the return of the 'same' still repeats that, which had been buried and, which travels with us. However, it does so in a way that is open to new potentials for being in the world. Hope is essential to this opening, repeating our sense of being a fugitive in language differently; to taking flight from the paralyzing anxiety of the black hole in my head and turning it inside out.

Hospital is a long time ago and can't be generalised to the whole of mental health services. There are good and bad teams everywhere and, if a whole team is rotten, it is unfair to blame the weakest member. I was just unlucky in the care I did (not) receive. The delusion unravelled at precisely a point where I had enough critical tools to make a different set of meanings and rebuild 'myself'. In this 'rebuilding', I learned to cover my ears from the noise of chaos and affirm it at the limit of what I can do. Philosophers have had a tendency to romanticise encounter with Eternal Return but while many talk the talk, very few walk the walk (or if they do, they don't admit to ever having spent time off the rational calendar). There is nothing romantic or heroic about losing your sense of skin in the world. My episodes were extreme, extended and horrifying. I nearly killed myself in the graveyard delusion because I could endure it no longer. Cutting out new skin was a brute question of survival, aided by needing to be a mother to my son, making it possible to get around without feeling too anxious all the time. It isn't possible to throw that kind of stuff away but it is possible to make it do some useful work. I still oscillate between going too fast mentally (the spaceship) and being in the doing of the now (the fly). However, I like both modes of being in the world and can do useful work with both in a manageable spectrum. The most 'inhuman' parts have been turned into mechanisms, a kind of second immune system that maintains a sense of skin in the world and sheds it at the same time. This is meshed with my autonomic functions and seemed the least aggressive repetition of affects that are parts of me, paranoia and its persecutory other, violence and its violated 'other'. I chose not to turn these outwards at the time and this choice has been tested and remains robust. However, I have no choice about writing to channel these affects. It is okay to chop up dead texts – not so good to turn the impulse on the living!

Few people get the opportunity to be their own underwriter and, at times, I still elevate into complex operations. At these times, I am practically capable of very little (other than controlling my flight) and present as quite vulnerable on the ground. I avoid people at all costs at these times. I'm not a bad pilot around anxiety and anger spirals but there are distinct limits to what else I can do when I am navigating them. It is also physically painful. People that only deal with practical living find it difficult to see that I am still there because they don't understand the multi-dimensional character of thought and emotion that go around the spectrum of anxiety most people consider sustainable. I need periods of withdrawal when these dimensions become too big to deal with the human race as well!

In hope we live and learn. We do not believe in the resurrection and we do not watch zombie films. If I am living with an illness today, I do not want a cure for it. My (ex) father cannot be blamed for not having the emotional resource to bring up children alone. I would not choose to be another person and this means acceptance of the past in the changing plane of the present. Acceptance does not imply consent. I cannot change what has been but I can assert my no to parts of this in and outside of a personal life. Strictly speaking, the future is an open category. It is projected on, like a mirror, by beliefs and attitudes which, in turn, inform the way the past and present are conceived. Dancing with difference repeats traumatic events differently, configuring new possibilities for being in the world[8]. In this way, it is possible to think of the episodes as part of a process of affective transformation, re-covering the horror with a more joyful tonality of soul.

## Some thoughts on good practice

- What would have really helped in hospital would have been people with the patience to listen and find out about me. I needed people to take the time to explain what was going on around me.
- Focus on what I could do rather than on what I would not be able to achieve would have removed some of the obstacles to well-being. Every negative can be turned into a positive. Look at the skills involved in surviving an episode and try to work with them.
- Some friendly faces would have helped alleviate the fear at the time. Medication might have been a short-term option through the worst parts of my recovery journey, if my relationship

to it was not so traumatic. If somebody really believes they are going to die in their sleep don't wake them up for sleeping tablets! If somebody doesn't want to take their medication find out why before you judge them to be 'non-compliant'. Some of the side effects are worse than the condition. Why not make it clear from the start that medication is a trial and error process and involve the person on the receiving end more fully in the process? I had to live a fugitive life to remain medication free. Unless I am threatening to murder my neighbours, surely I have the right to an informed choice in these decisions.

- Look at the functionality of what appears to you to be a delusion. All of mine did therapeutic work, alternative realities that cushioned me from some quite devastating life experiences until I was ready to deal with them. Don't mock someone's spiritual or intellectual beliefs just because they are alien to you. It is really hard living in a world that no one else inhabits. There are no friends in it and nobody to talk to.

- Honest acceptance and some sensitive handling would have been helpful. I am still able to strike up relations with frightened animals because I relate to them. If you have never felt this, at least make room for it. When I am experiencing psychosis, I am hypersensitive to what is going on around me and feel this in my body. A harsh tone of voice can feel like being shot and reverbs through my nervous system. When I am not experiencing psychosis, I can still hear the back tone if someone is being dishonest with me or pretending to be interested. Don't fake your concern as this is worse than being left alone. There is a whole layer of non-verbal communication that can be tuned in to if you are really interested in establishing rapport with someone who is experiencing psychosis.

- Recovery may be a life process for a person. Workers with the modesty to see themselves as a step in a bigger process are the kinds of workers that will continue to work hopefully, even if they see no immediate result. Patience is an underrated quality in holding hope for a person, especially in services orientated around short-term results. Those that have it do wonderful work even if it is the next worker down the line that will see the fruit of their labour.

- Trusting relations between experts of their experience and clinical experts is essential. I am fortunate today that I have a great GP with whom it is possible to say I am near the limit of my stress thresholds and get a sick note before the balance tips too far. This makes it possible for me to work full-time most of the time although I have to say that there are a lot of unsympathetic employers out there. Mental health services are the worst at looking after their own. There is no such thing as a well-being note but someone ought to invent it. That way, I could have prevented some long absences. I would love this to be as straightforward as a course of antibiotics. Good self-management is not about going at it alone. It is about honest and discrimination-free relations with professional experts who also recognise and work with your expertise to optimise best mental health.

- A genuine desire to find out about people who are experiencing psychosis. Staff willing to come out of their offices would be a good first step towards the above. I know there is lots of paperwork but if that is all that you are doing then you are hiding from your role (in case it makes more paperwork!).

- Don't generalise from a model! People that experience psychosis rarely fit neatly under a general explanatory framework. Don't impose your interpretation on a person's experience. Listen to how someone is making sense of their experience and try to establish a conversation between your and their understanding. It would have been easier to put down the spaceship and fly delusions if I had been able to say that was how I was experiencing myself.

- People working with me to build/support confidence, self-esteem and a sense of belonging. When I have this sense, I am capable of a lot. When it is undermined, I still find it hard to leave the house.

- Services need to shift their thinking from what does the service need to what do the people who use the service need, and how can we best support people to support this. A genuine service orientation is not about not having an ego. Nobody, with the possible exception of Buddha is without an ego. Services that expect this from their staff are actually looking for a slave orientation. As a mental health professional, I have encountered this attitude many times and each time come away thinking small wonder that staff feel disempowered or, at worst case, are abusive to people in their care. The very first time I spoke to a mental health employer about the themes outlined above I was called egocentric because I had put 'my anxiety' first. If staff support needs are recognised and met, it might be sustainable for them to put their ego second to the needs of people who experience psychosis on a daily basis.

Finally, supporting people to find their own recovery pathways makes me feel better! As well as wanting to support the person, it generates a sense of rescue for the bits of me that were not supported and are still difficult at times. I am reflexive about this in practice and don't rescue but remain strongly motivated by the desire to deliver a service I would have wanted to participate in and change attitudes towards people that don't fit the norm. Contemporary services remain a source of great hope in this project. There has been a sea of change in attitudes and a willingness to listen to what psychosis can do that was unimaginable in the 80s and 90s. If there had been good care then, I would not have achieved anything like the emotional width I have today. While it is not a path to responsibly recommend, the self-discipline to solve complex problems was made in extremes of these experiences. Speculative thought is a violent and protracted process. To be any good at it, you need the mind set of a serial killer and the restraint not to become one! My episodes gave me that discipline and my son gave the love with which to temper this with care for the living. Most important, he has not become a victim and is developing into a sensitive, insightful young man. He is able to laugh and say that if I ever become completely sane he will 'disown' me! This acceptance is priceless. I experience tremendous joy in transforming the present plane of possibility and have moved to a position where it is possible to feel genuine love for people without resentment, even though they still hurt my ears from time to time. There is no way back to before and I would not wish it to be so, despite times when the 'black hole' seems big again. The event of becoming psychotic continues to exert a profound and positive influence on what I am and am capable of becoming. I would have gone truly mad without these episodes. It is at the edge of reason that we love life and love laughter, re-covering recovery in the hope of people yet to come.

There is (no place) like home

## Endnotes

1. It was not possible within this narrative to convey my experiences authentically. The use of different fonts hints at experiences that are disjointed, which reconnect to each other to give a kind of sense. The primary sources are my PhD (Nietzsche and Feminism(s): doing time beyond the ends of 'women'), private poetry, and an oral interview I have given for *Psychosis Revisited*, which describes three episodes. These sources interplay throughout the narrative voices. There are two narrative voices – a young and an older voice, but it should be born in mind that both are reconstructed from the standpoint of the present, in relation to the future, they hope to be.

2. Jacques Derrida was the frontrunner of deconstruction in continental philosophy up until his death in 2004. A prolific writer, his famous statement that there is '*nothing outside the text*' (1974) and his signature motif of *différance* forms the backdrop of our writing. *Différance* is a term worked out at many points in Derrida's ouevre. At its simplest, it is a play on the French word

*différer*, meaning both 'to defer' and 'to differ' simultaneously. *Différance* stands in a critical relationship to phenomenological and psychoanalytic perspectives on memory, meaning and repetition. For Derrida, meaning is both present and absent, it is also perpetually displaced and postponed; the gap between sign and signified can never be closed down nor contained within phenomenological brackets.

3. Hegel, Descartes and Socrates are canonical figures in the Western philosophical tradition. Readers interested in exploring the relation between these philosophers and madness, for further reading refer to 'madness and cogito' in Derrida's (1978) *Writing and Difference*.

4. Martin Luther (1483–1586) was the founding father of Protestantism. Originally a Catholic, he critiqued the corruption of the system of indulgences under Pope Leo X. Salvation for Luther could not be purchased by this worldly works but was achievable on the grounds of faith alone. As the son of a Lutheran minister, Nietzsche's proclamation that '*God is dead*' is framed within this tradition, reversing the emphasis on faith to worldly deeds.

5. Nietzsche's riddle is also doing battle with Plato. Plato's idea of truth is based on original models which are copied by people. Like religion, Plato places one (unachievable) idea of the good as the highest eternal form. Without the elevation of one term, there would be no way of arguing for the proper property of the other virtues, for example justice. While the first term may be irrecoverable, it is presented as an immaterial reality to which successive instants lay claim and by which their rights as claimants is 'judged' (Widder, 2002)

6. The Eternal Return of the Same is the literal belief that history repeats itself identically. Although no one has lived long enough to empirically test this hypothesis, the evidence against it is compelling.

7. If everything is transitory, joy cannot be eternal in the way inferred by the Eternal Return of the Same. In *Thus Spoke Zarathustra*, the second dance song juxtaposes woe and joy '*the world is deep, deeper than day can comprehend.... Deep is its woe, joy, deeper than heart's agony ... woe says fade! go! ... but all joy wants eternity, wants deep, deep, deep eternity*' (Nietzsche, 1969, p.244–245). These lines are usually used to support the case for the 'same' with which I disagree – hence the reversal made above.

8. Readers wishing to know more about 'dancing with difference' from a theoretical and performance perspective can refer to Briginshaw & Chandler (2009).

## References

Briginshaw V & Chandler R (2009) *Rethinking Temporality: Intertextual plays within and between discourses of space, time and performing bodies*. In: V Briginshaw & R Burt *Writing Dancing Together*, London: Palgrave Macmillan.

Derrida J (1974) *Of Grammatology*, (trs) Spivak GC. Baltimore: John Hopkins University Press.

Derrida J (1978) *Writing and Difference*, (trs) Bass A. London & New York: Routledge and Kegan Paul.

Deleuze G (1994) *Difference and Repetition*, (trs) Patton P. London: Athlone.

Deleuze G (2006) *Nietzsche and Philosophy*, (trs) Tomlinson H. London: Continuum International Publishing Group Ltd.

Klossowski P (1997) Nietzsche and the Vicious Circle, (trs) Smith DW. London: Athlone Press.

Nietzsche F (1969) *Thus Spoke Zarathustra – A book for everyone and no one*, (trs) Hollingdale RJ. London: Penguin.

Nietzsche F (1974) *The Gay Science: With a prelude of rhymes and appendix of songs*, (trs) Kaufman W. New York: Vintage Books.

Oliver K (1995) *Womanizing Nietzsche: Philosophy's relation to the feminine*. London: Routledge.

Widder N (2002) *Genealogies of Difference*. Chicago: University of Illinois Press.

## Bibliography

Baudrillard J (1996) *The Perfect Crime*. London & New York: Verso Books.

Baum F (1956) *The Wizard of Oz*. New York: Scholastic Press.

Derrida J (1979) *Spurs: Nietzsche's styles*. Chicago: The University of Chicago Press.

Freud S (2001) *Totem and Taboo*. London: Routledge.

Heidegger M (1962) *Being and Time*, (trs) Macquarry J. London: SCM Press.

Heidegger M (1982) *Nietzsche: The Eternal Recurrence of the Same* (Nietzsche, Vols III & IV, (trs) Krell TF). New York: Harper Collins.

Irigaray L (1985) *Speculum of the Other Woman*, (trs) Gill G. New York: Cornell University Press.

Irigaray L (2004) *An Ethics of Sexual Difference*, (trs) Gill G. New York: Continuum International Publishing Group Ltd.

Lacan J (1977) *Écrits*, (trs) Sheridan A. New York: WW Norton & Co.

Lacan J (1977) *The Four Fundamental Concepts of Psychoanalysis*, (eds) Jacques- Miller A, (trs) Sheridan A. New York: WW Norton & Co.

Segal J (1992) *Melanie Klein*. Taylor & Francis: Sage Publications Ltd.

# Conclusion

Mark Hayward and Ruth Chandler

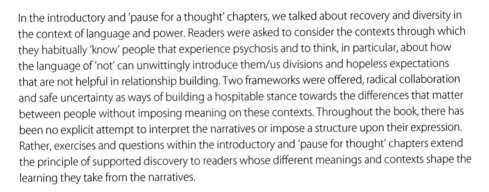

In the introductory and 'pause for a thought' chapters, we talked about recovery and diversity in the context of language and power. Readers were asked to consider the contexts through which they habitually 'know' people that experience psychosis and to think, in particular, about how the language of 'not' can unwittingly introduce them/us divisions and hopeless expectations that are not helpful in relationship building. Two frameworks were offered, radical collaboration and safe uncertainty as ways of building a hospitable stance towards the differences that matter between people without imposing meaning on these contexts. Throughout the book, there has been no explicit attempt to interpret the narratives or impose a structure upon their expression. Rather, exercises and questions within the introductory and 'pause for thought' chapters extend the principle of supported discovery to readers whose different meanings and contexts shape the learning they take from the narratives.

Being true to this non-interpretative aspiration has not been easy, as each of the editors hold descriptions of their worlds that act as lenses through which to understand the worlds of other people. One is a husband, father, committed Christian and supporter of West Ham United Football Club; a blue belt in Karate; a keen writer and researcher who desires to use these skills to influence the understandings and practice of others within mental health services; a director of a youth charity that seeks to establish places where young people can safely grow and learn; and someone who struggles to maintain a work–life balance. One is a committed atheist who is football adverse; single parent and grandparent to be; a cultural critic/creative writer; interested in theology, linguistics and philosophy (continental); likes cooking; likes animals; is an intermittent gardener and photographer, likes bowling and kite flying and a lover of blue cheese and chocolate ice cream (sometimes together). She is also a person who has experienced psychosis and is keen to influence the understanding and practice of others. She struggles, sometimes, with being intelligible to anyone except herself! Both editors are, or have been, frontline mental health workers.

In the language of 'not', these contexts are, at points, mutually exclusive. The editorial 'experiment' of this collection was to find out if genuine collaboration between fundamentally different world views was a realistic aspiration. It would be wholly pointless to make practice recommendations that we could not achieve ourselves! Our conclusion is that relationship building with people whose views challenge your own is hard work at times but worth the struggle! Core beliefs are an important part of feeling safe in the world. However, there is nothing in radical collaboration or safe uncertainty that suggests that one should abandon one's core beliefs. Rather, a position of authoritative doubt is one that chooses to maintain core beliefs while recognising that safe certainty about them is impossible.

Attempting to be open-minded when working with someone who is experiencing psychosis will be similarly difficult. Mental health workers will need to be aware of their own lenses and how these might facilitate or impede sufficient open-mindedness; they will need to be aware of the language they use to describe difference, and the interpretative habits that have become normative in the contexts where they encounter people who experience psychosis; they will need to be conscious of the need to collaborate 'radically' and sometimes resist a well-intentioned desire to fix things for the client; and they will need to tolerate, understand and work with the uncertainty that may be generated by an exploration of worlds that may be very different from their own, and seem frightening. A tall order?

In the author's meeting, it was requested that a 'lessons learned' section be included in the conclusion. To do this with minimal interpretation from the editors, the authors of the narratives were asked to distil the lessons learnt from their experiences into practice points that could assist mental health workers to address the challenges outlined above. While it has been important for the editors not to interpret in the collection process, the desire to understand these lessons after the event can only be co-constructed from their respective frames of reference. Accordingly, we highlight these in response to three of the questions that were asked of the reader at the end of the introductory chapter. To make best use of this section, it is recommended that readers revisit the questionnaire and note any core themes and/or changes in their response. It may be helpful to list your thoughts alongside the sections below.

## Hospitality to difference

**Question 1:** Who am I? Write a short description of your world. This can include, but is not limited to, personal qualities; experience; skills; values; cultural/social identity; likes and dislikes; friends; relationships etc.

Differences between people can relate to role and/or perspective. The anonymous author from chapter 7 raises awareness of a difference of role when he states that '*proper and meaningful involvement of the carers in the treatment of those suffering from mental ill health improves the outcome for both the person they care for and themselves*' (p.72). The difference here could relate to the role of a carer/relative to the person experiencing psychosis, as loss, trauma, confusion, distress and recovery may be experienced in dissimilar ways – a point emphasised by Mark (p.57), '*Do not mistake the needs of service users necessarily to be the same as those of their carers – they often differ and may conflict*'. Or the difference could relate to the varying roles of informal carer and paid worker, each of whom may want similar things for the person experiencing psychosis, but for whom collaboration may not be common or expected.

Role differences may also be apparent between the lives and lifestyles of the worker and the person experiencing psychosis. Not necessarily the differences that may be apparent within an equal opportunities monitoring form, but the differences relating to choices, vocational opportunities, networks of relationships and aspirations. How do these differences influence the ability of the worker and service user to collaborate radically? Mark suggests that the journey towards common ground and understanding must be given initial impetus by the worker, '*Try to get to where the service user is at rather than expect them to come to you*' (p.57). However, the process of learning within the relationship will need to be more reciprocal, with a commitment to the process that facilitates an open-minded approach to new possibilities, '*Accept that the relationship with service users is a two way street – you as workers must always strive to learn from your service users*' (Mark, p.58).

A difference of perspective can relate to understandings of and responses to psychotic experiences. Roy (p.43) asks for workers to '*Understand that paranoid thoughts are real for me. Some friendly reassurance helps me to have the confidence to think that not everyone is in conspiracy against me*'. Offering him an alternate world view or challenging his world view may not be productive. Rather, an acceptance of his world view and the unsafe consequences of it for him may be most productive. In this instance, such a perspective would enable a worker to intervene to maximise feelings of safety for the client – a point that is emphasised by Moira, '*When I am experiencing psychosis, take my fear about the Devil in the room seriously and don't leave me in that room. Keep me safe*' (p.84). There is not necessarily a call to share a belief that the Devil is real; rather Moira asks workers to empathise with the feelings that are likely to be generated by such a frightening perception.

The anonymous writer of Chapter 10 asks that hospitality to difference be extended beyond the distress of the moment to a consideration of the possible value of psychotic experiences in the longer term: '*Look at the functionality of what appears to you to be a delusion. All of mine did therapeutic work, alternative realities that cushioned me from some quite devastating life experiences until I was ready to deal with them*' (p.121). The challenges for the worker mount as he/she may need to consider the person's psychotic experiences as both a perceived threat to physical and emotional safety in the short term, and a fundamental aspect of psychological safety in the longer term.

**What lessons can you take from the practice points into your personal or professional development? How could you help people that experience psychosis to feel safe?**

# Communication

**Question 2:** Which of the above [responses to question one] do you believe could be best developed to support communication with people whose world may be very different from your own?

Throughout the narratives there is a strong sense of the value of workers listening to the person who is experiencing psychosis, '*Mental health workers have helped me through those more difficult times by listening, believing in me, taking risks and by supporting my decisions (even though at times the possible outcomes of those decisions are uncertain)*' (Becky, p.29). This process of listening may not always be easy, '*Be flexible in your approach – service users often communicate in a different way to workers*' (Mark, p.57) but it can be beneficial to both the worker, '*Understand how afraid I can feel at times and the strength of this feeling*' (Roy, p.42) and the person experiencing psychosis, '*Just having someone to give me time to allow the thoughts to come out. If you don't they stay in my head and grow*' (Moira, p.84). The reciprocal benefits of listening are further emphasised by the author of Chapter 10 as she reflects on the value of being heard within the process of making meaning, '*Listen to how a person is making sense of their experience and try to establish a conversation between your and their understanding. It would have been easier for me to put down the spaceship and fly delusions if I had been able to say that was how I was experiencing myself*' (p.121).

The value of a channel of communication is not restricted to listening and making sense of unusual experiences. Roy describes the healing properties of conversation per se, '*I don't always need to talk about my problems. Ordinary conversation about the weather or someone's dog with a broken leg does me more good than an injection or a tranquilizer'* (p.43), and Moira speaks of the need to receive information to aid understanding of unfamiliar contexts that can exacerbate distress, *'Medication and procedures like sectioning to be explained to alleviate anxiety and fear of the unknown'* (p.83).

**What lessons from the practice points would be most supportive of communication between mental health workers and people that experience psychosis?**

# Hope

**Question 5:** Can you think of any habits of speech or action in your workplace that are optimistic about people that experience psychosis?

Hope is an essential ingredient of any process of recovery, yet workers can often have low expectations for people experiencing mental health problems (Social Exclusion Unit, 2004). The authors suggest that an approach that is hopefully oriented towards recovery is one that is gradual, respectful of risk without being controlled by it, and based upon existing strengths. Becky emphasises the graduated nature of change by stating, *'If I have any advice to give to any one working with someone who has mental health difficulties, it is to encourage them, and to offer step-by-step support in making their own decisions. This might start off by someone making small decisions (which can seem huge at the time) but gradually at the individual's pace this will increase'* (p.30). Important within this assertion is the requirement that there is respect and support for the agency and decision-making of the person experiencing psychosis. This in itself may seem like an example of positive risk taking, as these decisions may be seen as less than rational and not concur with those that the worker/team/service may have chosen for that person. However, the consequences of not supporting positive risk taking are highlighted by Mark, *'Be prepared to take calculated risks – by not doing this it can reinforce how stuck some service users feel'* (p.57). The emphasis placed on 'calculated' seems important, as risks explored collaboratively between worker and service user will be those that are known about and can be jointly 'managed'. Collaborative risk management opens a space in which it is possible to explore the related understandings of safe and unsafe certainty or uncertainty held by each party. By having this conversation in a safe supported manner, it may be possible to start a movement away or negotiation with unhelpful notions of safe certainty that may be structuring the ground of present action.

A further way of managing risk and moving to a position of safe uncertainty is to enhance the likelihood of 'success' by working with the strengths of the person experiencing psychosis, *'Focus on what I could do rather than on what I would not be able to achieve would have removed some of the obstacles to well-being. Every negative can be turned into a positive. Look at the skills involved in surviving an episode and try to work with them'* (anonymous, p.120).

**How can you balance working with the strengths and skills of people who experience psychosis with the need to keep people safe?**

# Support and supervision

**Question 7:** How do you feel when a person talks to you about an idea or thought they have, which you think is unusual?

Hearing about experiences that are very different to one's own can generate considerable anxiety. In these uncertain situations, it would seem reasonable for a worker to seek safe certainty by imposing understandings upon psychotic experiences. Such imposed understandings may also protect the worker from the disclosure of the interpersonal trauma that is often revealed as connections between life events and psychotic experiences that are uncovered. If the call within the narratives is for the worker to listen and learn about the impact and possible meaning/function of psychotic experiences, this urge to impose needs to be resisted. These skills need to be fostered and supported. If the workers are expected to engage with the discomfort of not knowing in pursuit of supporting someone experiencing psychosis, how is this best achieved? It is not reasonable to expect frontline mental health workers to listen to difficult and potentially traumatic disclosures without a place to take their feelings about this. Mental health workers can expect to be supported in formal structures of supervision, yet the purpose and orientation of supervision can be variable, often with too great an emphasis upon management rather than development. The quality of supervision thus varies a great deal across the voluntary and statutory sectors and between community and inpatient settings. In some teams, it is taken as given that supporting the emotional well-being of the workforce is a core ingredient in the delivery of good-quality care for people who experience psychosis. How can frontline workers be expected to deal with anxieties and received hopelessness if nobody is listening to them? However, in organisational cultures that polarise between a start point of unsafe uncertainty and the (impossible) goal of safe certainty, supervision is more likely to be structured around performance indicators and checklists, making it difficult to open a space of supported discovery. In these situations, frontline mental health workers can feel thrown on their own resources to develop strategies for managing uncertainty in a constructive collaborative manner.

Emma's suggestions for people experiencing psychosis can also be applied to workers, as support can be derived from both the self, '*Reward yourself for your successes and don't be too hard on yourself when things take a step back, there is always tomorrow and recovery means getting over set backs too*' (p.98) and the identification and tapping of existing resources '*friends and abilities that will help you meet your goal*' (p.98). A supervisory space that is sufficiently encouraging of reflection and creativity can be found outside of formal service/professional structures and include peers and/or service user colleagues/consultants. Anne draws attention to the benefits she has derived from being supported by service users as, '*I have received the most sensitive and robust support from service user-led groups, support which has had the most positive impact on my well-being, I believe my self-directed support would take me again and again back to service user-led groups to find my 'balance*' and suggests that workers can learn much from such forums, '*Practitioners should work in partnership with people, genuine partnership where 'self governance' is dominate. Staff should know and support any local service user-led groups and indeed learn from such forums as they have so much to teach*' (p.38).

**What is the bottom line? If workers are to actively and innovatively support the recovery of people experiencing psychosis, they also require support and encouragement in order to promote their sense of efficacy and well-being.**

What kind of supervision do you have? If it is exclusively performance driven, do you see a need for a more person-centred approach to your development? If so, where could you get this from?

## Recovery to...?

It is recommended that readers take their own highlights from the narratives throughout as a basis for further thought about the issues and themes made visible. You may wish to revisit all the questions in the opening questionnaire or set out some new questions to think about. Here we remark that our concluding reflections cannot avoid the question of recovery to ... what? The notion of a journey without a destination is liberating if you do not like your process too heavily structured by outcomes and ends. However, the notion of 'ends' is deeply embedded in the Western tradition. It is extremely difficult to tell any kind of story without imposing an 'end' on it, even if this 'end' is also an opening onto something else. The very act of creating this book involved timelines, ends and summing up without which it would not be possible to move beyond them to a different place and different sets of possibilities. Similarly, it is difficult to work towards personal recovery goals without identifying (at least some of them) in advance. People who have not experienced psychosis might not understand how difficult it is to get out of bed without a sense of destination for that day, even if it is just to go to the local shop. It is possible to vary destinations en route and, we would suggest, positively beneficial to do so. There is nothing worse than working towards an 'end' you have changed your mind about. Having the flexibility to change the direction of travel without feeling like one has 'failed' in so doing, is an important part of meeting the challenge of living a meaningful life with continued symptoms.

The narratives presented here vary a great deal on the extent to which they see recovery as heading towards specific ends that can be achieved and the extent to which they see it as an open-ended process. Emma questions the notion of a recovery pathway needing to be unidirectional by suggesting that someone should '*Decide what you want to recover 'from' or 'to'*' (p.98). Whatever the direction of travel, she suggests that the destination may be varied and will be determined by the person experiencing psychosis '*This may be a job, a hobby, a physical health concern, an interest, a 'symptom' or a friendship among other things*' (p.98). Furthermore, Emma suggests that arrival at a recovery destination may need to be corroborated by a variety of perspectives '*Decide how you would know you were there, who else would notice? What point would be an acceptable level of success?*' (p.98).

Rather than focus upon a destination, Becky seems to value the process and the opportunities that can be encountered along the way '*I may not currently be able to do paid work on a full-time basis but through doing voluntary work I have built up my skills and confidence, felt valued, met inspirational people and given meaning to my life (opening up new avenues) whilst at the same time being able to vary the workload according to my health*' (p.29). For the author of Chapter 10, this process cannot be time limited insofar as achievements along the way may not be visible to any given worker '*Recovery may be a life process for a person. Workers with the modesty to see themselves as a step in a bigger process are the kinds of workers that will continue to work hopefully even if they see no immediate result. Patience is an underrated quality in holding hope for a person, especially in services orientated around short-term results. Those that have it do wonderful work even if it is the next worker down the line that will see the fruit of their labour*' (p.121). The call for patience when supporting recovery is echoed by Steve '*having time and being patient*' (p.19). Long-term patience is difficult in services that are not joined up and that involve a lot of wasted time in reinventing the wheel with each new worker. Steve also points to the importance of '*continuity of care*' (p.19) between the same or different people in supporting his recovery. It is also more difficult for people who experience psychosis to work towards personal recovery goals if these have to be re-explained and re-negotiated with each new worker.

**What further differences and similarities stand out for you between the understandings of recovery described throughout? List the themes that you could easily apply in your professional and/or personal development and the ones that may be more difficult. Ask yourself what is easy and difficult about them as a starting point for further consideration.**

## Recovery beyond...?

Concluding reflections about recovery and diversity also cannot avoid the question of recovery beyond individual aims and aspirations. As stated in the introduction, one of the challenges of thinking about recovery and diversity together is how to think about lots of different recovery goals, destinations and processes without subordinating them to one master goal or process under which the differences between people become invisible. The innovation of this collection has been to drop the 'them/us', ideologically and methodologically in order to have ordinary conservations about what recovery and psychosis means with some people that experience it. However, the collection does not presume to define what recovery is for all people in different contexts and locations. Nor does it presume to know what a person is for all people. Rather, we hope to have initiated ordinary conversations between the different actions, routines and statements that make up the everyday *habitus* of frontline mental health workers and people that experience psychosis; that is conversations in which different core beliefs may co-construct viable recovery pathways.

Future conversations will inevitably differ from the pathways we have taken and this is welcomed. The many contexts that make up the complexity of lived experience are always more than can be said from a single context or from a shared set of perspectives. To consider recovery and diversity together involves recognising that, potentially, there are as many recovery pathways as there are people on the planet! Recovery 'is' both the sum of the overlapping contexts and perspectives that make up the recovery-orientated practice in a location and a fluid spectrum of experience in excess of locally oriented practice.

In other words, recovery 'is' the collection of recovery pathways that make up a group of people at any given moment and can be enabled or disabled by the person's relationship with supporting services. At the level of individual narrative, what is significant in one recovery pathway may be of no value at all in another, rendering it invisible. It can be useful to become invisible, if by doing so you have made yourself redundant to the person who came to you for help! At the same time however, recovery thought of as a fluid spectrum of experience is also a multiple spectrum in change, becoming different from the past or present reality. Thinking of recovery in both of these ways, as always wider than the personal self or service identity, fosters the hospitality to difference we have discussed throughout, making it less credible to 'place' recovery under the banner of any practical or political agenda, whether this is service driven or service user led. If recovery is about how to live a meaningful life with the continued presence of 'symptoms', there must be a shift in service provision to supporting both processes and goals that are idiosyncratically defined amidst contexts that may not yet be known. Welcoming a person like a book you have not read or like a guest from another country is one way of opening conversation about these goals and processes, while remaining hospitable to the different worlds made visible in a space of safe 'uncertainty'. That is a space that does not appear to know in advance what people who experience psychosis can do or can become.

## References

Bourdieu P (1990) *The Logic of Practice*, (trs) Nice R. United Kingdom: Polity Press.

Social Exclusion Unit (2004) *Mental Health and Social Exclusion*. London: Office of the Deputy Prime Minister.

Voicing Psychotic Experiences: A reconsideration of recovery and diversity